engineering fundamentals

IN MEASUREMENTS

PROBABILITY

STATISTICS

AND DIMENSIONS

McGRAW-HILL GENERAL ENGINEERING SERIES

VERNON B. HAMMER, CONSULTING EDITOR

DUNN **introduction to digital computer problems using fortran IV**

SEABLOOM **vector algebra for engineers**

CRANDALL AND SEABLOOM **engineering fundamentals in measurements, probability, statistics, and dimensions**

About 20 billion measurements are
being made every day in this country—
in science, in industry, and in everyday life.
Robert D. Huntoon, Director,
National Bureau of Standards Institute
for Basic Standards

engineering fundamentals

Redwood Empire Association

IN MEASUREMENTS

PROBABILITY

STATISTICS

AND DIMENSIONS

KEITH C. CRANDALL
department of general engineering
university of washington

ROBERT W. SEABLOOM
department of general engineering
university of washington

new york
san francisco McGRAW-HILL BOOK COMPANY
st. louis
düsseldorf
london
mexico
panama
sydney
toronto

This book was set in Monophoto Times
Roman by Holmes Typography, Inc., and
printed on permanent paper and bound by
Peninsula Lithography Company. The
designer was Nancy Clark; the drawings
were done by Judith McCarty. The editors
were Roland S. Woolson, Jr., and Michael
A. Ungersma. Charles A. Goehring
supervised production.

engineering fundamentals IN MEASUREMENTS, PROBABILITY,
STATISTICS, AND DIMENSIONS

Printed in the United States of America.

Library of Congress catalog card number: 71-115140

1234567890   PEPE   79876543210

preface

This book introduces the fundamentals of probability, statistics, and dimensions as they relate to engineering measurements. Measurements are basic to every phase of engineering, and the engineer is usually the one ultimately accountable for interpreting and utilizing the results.

We have approached the study of measurements from the standpoint of statistical inference. The nature of physical measurements is discussed, and the basic precepts of mathematical probability and statistics are presented within the framework of engineering data. These principles are then extended to an analysis of samples and their underlying distributions, and mathematical approximations of distributions are developed for the purpose of making statistical inferences from engineering data. The effects of error propagation in the mathematical manipulation of data containing errors is examined, and finally, the rudiments of dimensional analysis are presented.

The Appendixes provide auxiliary information on the presentation of a problem and its solution, and on use of the slide rule, as well as discussions of significant figures, summation notation, derivations of error-propagation equations, and some pertinent tables. The References afford a guide to more advanced works in the various areas discussed.

We have attempted to keep the text on a clear and elementary level. All necessary derivations are shown in full, and each new concept or equation is illustrated by specific examples. The main topics are summarized at the end of each chapter. In addition, a large number of problems are provided to facilitate practical application of the concepts and principles presented. As an aid to independent study and to provide an immediate check, answers are provided for all problems except those requiring graphic solution.

The text is designed to meet a variety of needs. It is specifically written for introductory engineering courses that combine the study of measurement theory, statistics, and unit systems, since the three are really inseparable. For students who do not have a calculus background, it should be appropriate for an introductory college-level statistics course and for statistics courses at junior colleges. In addition, it should be adaptable to introductory engineering problems courses and as a supplement to surveying textbooks.

We would like to express our appreciation to our colleagues in the Department of General Engineering at the University of Washington for their help and suggestions. In particular, we should like to thank Prof. W. L. Dunn, H. Boehmer, and M. O. Ness for reading and criticizing parts of the manuscript. Finally, we are grateful to Miss Carolyn Darcy, Mrs. Sharon Field, and Mrs. Edna Ossa for typing the manuscript.

KEITH C. CRANDALL
ROBERT W. SEABLOOM

contents

APPENDIXES

engineering fundamentals

IN MEASUREMENTS

PROBABILITY

STATISTICS

AND DIMENSIONS

one

introduction to engineering measurements

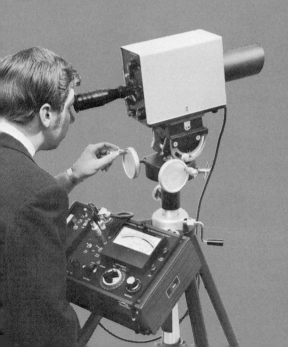

The present-day professional engineer must know the basic laws of mathematics, physics, chemistry, and economics in order to solve the problems involved in producing the things people need and want. Achievements of the engineering profession are evidenced in one form or another in practically every modern convenience, device, structure, and process. Engineers deal in such a vast number of areas that it is difficult to define the field of engineering concisely; for example, at the present time there are over fifty recognized engineering specialties. However, among currently accepted definitions of engineering is one proposed by the Engineering Council for Professional Development:

> Engineering is the profession in which knowledge of the mathematical and physical sciences gained by study, experience, and practice is applied with judgment to develop ways to utilize, economically, the materials and forces of nature for the progressive well being of mankind.

It is the concern with economics that distinguishes engineering from pure science. Whereas economic considerations are generally of secondary concern—and may even in some instances be of no concern—to the pure scientist, the function of the engineer is to achieve a more efficient process and a more economical end product.

The evolution of a product, from its conception to physical existence, is directed by engineering plans which are a culmination of all the creative processes known as *engineering design.* Design is a creative problem-solving process in which the engineer, working within predetermined bounds, converts technical information and ideas into useful products. Measurements are a fundamental part of engineering design.

The modern engineer is also becoming increasingly involved in the gathering of information to serve as a basis for new designs and the improvement of present ones. This process, known as *engineering research*, differs from pure research in that the goal is not merely knowledge, but the eventual implementation of that knowledge in a specific application. Measurements are a fundamental part of engineering research.

The process of implementing the basic discoveries relating to an engineering problem is referred to as *engineering development*. As part of this process a prototype of the item under study is generally produced. For items scheduled for mass production this is an integral part of the design process. Measurements are a fundamental part of engineering development.

Engineering production is the process of manufacturing an item according to the engineer's designs and specifications and ensuring that the resulting product is a faithful representation of his prototype. It is also important to ensure that all parts of the finished product actually perform as he has specified. Measurements are a fundamental part of engineering production.

After an engineering design has become the reality of a machine, a building or facility, or perhaps an industrial process, the finished product must be properly maintained and operated. This important task of *engineering operations and maintenance* entails regulating and evaluating complex machinery and processes for the most economical production of the desired end product. Measurements are a fundamental part of engineering operations and maintenance.

All these phases of engineering are integrally associated with the making of measurements and gathering of observational data. After the measurements have been made, they must be properly organized, interpreted, and evaluated before they can be utilized. Even the advantages provided by the high-speed computer depend on the accuracy of the input data, which usually are in the form of measurements. Moreover, some inherent operating characteristics of the computer tend to produce slight errors. Thus it is essential that the engineer be familiar with the theory and practice of making and employing measurements.

1-2 DEFINITION OF MEASUREMENT

A *measurement* is a comparison of an unknown quantity with a predefined standard, made by means of a measuring device. Hence any measured value is an *approximation* of the true or exact value, not the exact value itself. Since the exact value cannot be measured, a measurement contains, by definition, an *inherent error*.

In addition, the very act of making a measurement occasionally alters the quantity or condition being measured, and thus produces a discrepancy. For example, the insertion of a temperature-measuring probe into a liquid will slightly alter the temperature of the liquid. If an electric current is measured by connecting an ammeter in the circuit, the resistance of the meter itself will lower the measured current value in the circuit. These effects are for the most part negligible, and we will disregard them in this text.

Most measurements must be expressed in terms of both *magnitude* and *units*. It would be meaningless to report a measurement as just a number, say 15, or as just a unit, say pounds. Both a numerical value and a unit of measure must be given if the result is to have any meaning. Some values used in engineering can be expressed as pure number (a dimensionless quantity), but these are exceptions which will be discussed later. Units of measure usually describe size, amount, position, or time. The science that deals with measurements and their units is known as *metrology*. Most countries maintain official measurement standards from which secondary standards and legal definitions of certain quantities have been derived, mainly for industrial use. This is a separate topic and will be discussed in Chapter Seven.

1-3 METHODS OF MEASUREMENT

Measurements provide the quantitative information that is necessary to engineering design, development, research, and operations and maintenance. Measurements may be made with a device or instrument that measures either *directly* or *indirectly*.

direct comparison

Simple linear measurements are usually made directly. For example, the length of a tabletop may be measured by direct comparison with a standard yardstick (see Fig. 1-1). Many computed quantities are derived from direct measurements. For example,

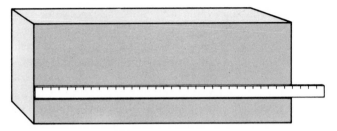

figure *1-1*   *Direct measurement of length*

velocity can be computed from direct measurements of distance and time. The exactness of the computed result is, of course, a function of the original measurements.

indirect comparison

Although measurement by direct comparison is very simple, it is not always the most accurate method. Our human faculties are often not sensitive enough to do a satisfactory job even when the instrument is capable of giving a satisfactory result. Also, the human senses are just not equipped to make measurements of some quantities. To determine the pH value of a solution, the strain in a steel bar, or the voltage in an electric circuit we must employ a more sophisticated type of measurement that entails indirect comparison with a standard. In this case the measuring apparatus and associated equipment record the raw measurement data as input and convert it to a form of output that is detectable to the human senses. In modern industry and technology the slower and more tedious direct-measurement devices have largely been supplanted by a great variety of instruments which record measurement information and convert it to a convenient display form.

An example of such an indirect-measurement device is the simple pressure gage shown in Fig. 1-2. The quantity we wish to measure is the pressure in the vessel. The pipe acts as a data-transmission tube, so that the data output may be displayed at a remote station. In this case the primary sensing device is the piston, which converts the fluid pressure into a resultant force on the piston rod;

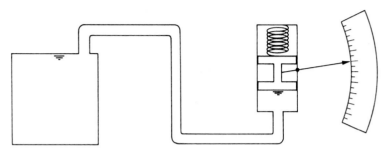

figure 1-2 *Indirect measurement of pressure with a pressure gage*

this force is in turn transmitted to the spring, creating a force differential and a resultant displacement. The displacement of the piston can be magnified by means of a linkage system so that the pointer displacement on the dial is more easily discernible.

Another device, known as a *Parshall flume*, measures the amount of water flowing in an irrigation ditch. An observer standing on the bank reads the water height on the gage and then computes the flow from a calibration chart (Fig. 1-3).

With both of these fundamental types of measuring devices the measurement can be determined only by making a reading, generally from a *graduated scale*. The difficulty in making readings from the scale and then converting the results constitutes the basic measuring problem.

figure 1-3 *Indirect measurement of water flow with a Parshall flume*

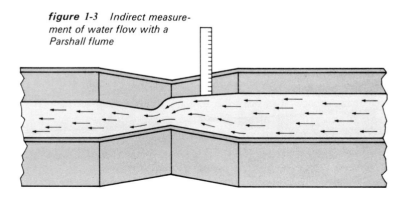

1-4 TERMINOLOGY OF MEASUREMENT

Although the actual measuring process may be carried out by others, the engineer in charge of the work is ultimately responsible for analyzing and interpreting the results. The subsequent use and reliability of the measurement data can be no better than the original measurements; hence it is the responsibility of the engineer to determine the method and number of measurements needed. This important function necessitates a knowledge of the fundamental terminology of measurement.

individual or single measurements

A *single* or *individual measurement* is a single reading or a succession of readings taken with all conditions the same except time. The exactness of a measurement cannot be increased merely by taking repeated readings with the same procedure and measuring device. However, as we shall see in later chapters, techniques from the field of mathematical statistics enable us to refine measurements beyond the capability of the measuring instrument, to a point more closely approaching the true value. Successive single measurements made under similar conditions with the same apparatus may not necessarily agree in value, but they will exhibit a statistical regularity or tendency to cluster around a central value. Suppose that two successive measurements of a distance give $8\frac{3}{8}$ in. and $8\frac{1}{2}$ in. on a ruler graduated to eighths of an inch. By taking the arithmetic mean, we obtain a value of $8\frac{7}{16}$ in., even though the ruler is not graduated to sixteenths of an inch. More on this later.

multiple measurements

A *multiple measurement* is series of measurements of a given quantity by different and independent procedures and with different measuring devices. For example, to accumulate a multiple measurement of the pressure of liquid in a vessel we would have to make measurements not only with the pressure gage shown earlier, but with separate and independent measuring devices as well. Whether to rely on single measurements of a quantity or employ a more sophisticated and expensive system that will produce multiple measurements is another decision that must be made by the engineer.

accuracy and precision

In the discussion of measurements and their associated errors frequent mention is made of accuracy and precision. To the layman these terms may be synonymous, but in the technical language of the engineer and scientist they have different meanings. *Accuracy* is the correctness or exactness with which a measured value represents the true value—in other words, its nearness to the true or established value. The true value itself cannot, of course, be measured by any physical means. *Precision* is the reproducibility of a measurement or the consistency of a set of measurements—in other words, the nearness of the individual measurements to each other.

It is possible for a group of measurements to be precise without being accurate. That is, the results may be consistent but bear no relationship to the true value. Conversely, it is possible for measurements to be relatively accurate, in that their mean gives a result very close to the true value, and yet be widely dispersed around this mean, indicating poor precision.

To clarify this relationship between accuracy and precision, consider the analogy of rifle marksmanship.* Compare the four targets depicted in Fig. 1-4.

Marksman A has shown good precision; the shots are closely grouped. He has also shown good accuracy; all the shots fall within the bull's-eye.

*J. M. Juran, "Quality Control Handbook," 2d ed., McGraw-Hill Book Company, New York, 1962; "Standard Methods for the Examination of Water Sewage, and Industrial Wastes," 10th ed., American Public Health Association, Inc., New York, 1955; B. Austin Barry, "Engineering Measurements," John Wiley & Sons, Inc., New York, 1964.

figure 1-4 *Shot patterns of four marksmen*

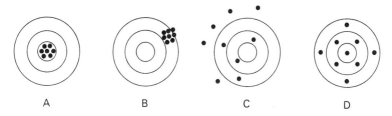

A   B   C   D

Marksman B has indicated good precision because all the shots are closely grouped, but his accuracy is relatively poor; none of his shots hit the bull's-eye.

Marksman C has shown both poor precision and poor accuracy. Not only are his shots widely scattered, but the average of these shots would not fall within the bull's-eye.

Marksman D shows poor precision in the wide dispersion of his shots and doubtful accuracy. Even though most of his shots missed the bull's-eye, it is possible statistically for the average of his shots to fall within the bull's-eye. Hence we cannot be absolutely sure of his accuracy and must designate it as doubtful.

Consider how we would apply these terms in describing measured parts. An accurate part is one with measurements that fall within a permissible range of sizes whose mean or central value is the value specified by the standard. Accuracy is the criterion of whether the part is acceptable. Precise parts may have measurements that fall within a rather narrow range, but this may or may not be the particular range that surrounds the specified value. Hence precision is not a criterion for acceptability.

reliability

Let us return to the target analogy, but consider only two targets with five shots each, as shown in Fig. 1-5. It is obvious that marksman F has shown better precision than marksman E because of the closer grouping of his shots. We see that statistically the mean of each set of shots is the same, indicating that marksmen E and F have both shot with the same accuracy. Nevertheless, we would immediately judge that F is a better shot than E because his shooting is more reliable. If marksmen E and F were each to fire another five shots, there is a good probability that F would again hit the bull's-eye five times and that E would again spray his shots. However, it is not too likely that he would spray them so fortuitously every time.

In terms of probability, marksman F is more likely to perform without failure than marksman E. In other words, F is more *reliable* than E. We may define reliability, then, as the probability of performing without failure a specified function under given conditions

figure *1-5 Shot patterns of marksmen E and F*

                           E   F

for a specified period of time.* Reliability is an evaluation of future performance. In terms of measurements, it is a prediction of the accuracy and precision of measurements to be taken in the future, which we base on the accuracy and precision of measurements already taken. We will discuss several measures of reliability in later chapters.

sensitivity

The accuracy of any measured value depends on the sensitivity of the measuring device, or the degree to which the device is capable of registering discernible differences. The measuring instrument must be able to detect the change and indicate it in some observable form. In indirect-measurement systems minute changes may be magnified many times at the readout level so that they are clearly discernible to the observer (see Fig. 1-6). The scale discrimination of the readout device must, of course, be fine enough to match the sensitivity of the measuring device. Modern technology is placing increasingly rigorous demands on instrument manufacturers for equipment that will make measurements with greater accuracy and precision and display them with less chance of mistake.

SUMMARY

All phases of engineering are integrally associated with making measurements, interpreting and evaluating them, and then utilizing the results toward a specific goal. A measurement is a comparison of an unknown quantity with some predefined standard; hence any measurement contains an inherent error.

*"Reliability of Military Electronic Equipment," Advisory Group on Reliability of Electronic Equipment, Washington, D.C., 1957.

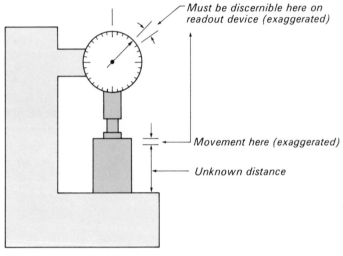

figure 1-6 A typical readout device

Measurements are made either by direct comparison of the measuring device with the item to be measured or by any of a number of indirect-measurement methods, in which the measuring device converts the basic information to a form detectable by the observer. Most engineering measurements are made by some form of indirect comparison.

The accuracy of a measured value is its exactness, or the degree to which it approaches the true or established value. Precision is the reproducibility of a measured value, or the degree to which a set of values approach each other. Reliability is a prediction of the future performance of a measuring instrument, or about future measurements, based on the data already obtained. Sensitivity refers to the minimum amount of change that a measuring device is capable of detecting and indicating.

PROBLEMS

1-1 Name the four fundamental aspects of engineering in which measurements are needed.

1-2   What is one word that best describes accuracy?

1-3   What is one word that best describes precision?

1-4   Is it possible to have a precise set of measurements that are not accurate? Explain.

1-5   Is it possible to have an accurate set of measurements that are not precise? Explain

1-6   If a marksman fired one shot into the bull's-eye, how would you describe his accuracy and precision?

1-7   Describe the two general types of measurement.

1-8   Explain how you would check the precision of a set of measurements.

1-9   Explain how you would check the accuracy of a set of measurements.

1-10   Why do all measurements contain errors?

1-11   What is generally needed in addition to a numerical value to express a measurement?

1-12   What is a measurement?

1-13   If a marksman fired one shot at a target on three consecutive days and hit the bull's-eye only on the first day, how would you describe his reliability?

1-14   What determines the accuracy of a single measurement?

1-15   In a certain factory all the clocks are controlled by electric impulses, so that they all indicate the correct time exactly to the second.

    a   How would you describe this time system?

    b   Even though the clocks are synchronized, they occasionally do not indicate the correct time, owing to power failure. When this happens how would you describe the system?

two

measurement errors

Boeing

2-1 *INHERENT ERROR IN MEASUREMENT*

As we saw in Chapter One, a measurement is a comparison with a predetermined standard. Hence a measured value is merely a representation of the desired exact value, not the exact value itself. Let us clarify this point by distinguishing between measuring and counting. It would be perfectly feasible to count the exact number of students in a class, but if we were to add the weights of each student and then divide the total weight by the average weight per student, our result would probably be a fractional value that differed slightly from the exact count. Thus a count gives an exact value, provided no mistakes are made, whereas a measurement, whatever its nature, can never give the exact value; by definition it must always contain an inherent error.

Note that a mistake and an error are not the same thing. A *mistake* is a blunder caused by human inattention or instrumental malfunction. An *error* is the difference between a measured value and the true exact value, and it follows statistical laws. Although the magnitude of the error is usually a function of the ability and skill of the observer and the sensitivity and reliability of the measuring device, the *presence* of an error is beyond human control.

Since the true value can never be measured, it follows that the magnitude of the error—the amount of deviation from the true value—cannot be measured either. However, errors do follow statistical laws, and we may deal with them by the techniques of mathematical statistics. Let us begin with some more concise definitions of error. ERRORS ⟶ FOLLOW STATISTICAL LAWS.

absolute error

The *absolute error* of any measurement is the difference between the measured value and the true value. Absolute error is independent of the magnitude of the measured value and does not in itself indicate the accuracy of the measurement. For example, an error of 2 amp in an electric-current reading of 500 amp represents an absolute error of 2 amp; if the electric current were 100 amp, the absolute error would still be 2 amp.

Let us designate the absolute error as E_a. We may then define

ABSOLUTE ERROR
⟶ INDEPENDENT OF THE MAGNITUDE OF THE MEASURED VALUE.

it in symbolic terms as

$$E_a = X_t - X_m \qquad \textbf{2-1}$$

where X_t is the true value and X_m is the measured value.

Since the true value X_t is never attainable, a logical question at this point is whether the absolute error E_a is also never attainable. As a practical solution we determine the *apparent* absolute error, which is the difference between the measured value and the best value of a series of measurements. We will discuss this further in Chapter Four.

relative error

The *relative error* of a measurement is the absolute error divided by the measured value. It can be expressed in symbolic terms as

$$E_r = \frac{E_a}{X_m} = \frac{X_t - X_m}{X_m} \qquad \textbf{2-2}$$

where E_r = relative error
$\quad\quad E_a$ = absolute error
$\quad\quad X_m$ = the measured value

Again, the best value obtained from a series of measurements would be substituted for X_t.

Consider the previous example of a 2-amp error in a 500-amp current reading. Whereas the absolute error in this case is 2 amp, the relative error as computed from Eq. 2-2 is

$$E_r = \frac{E_a}{X_m} = \tfrac{2}{500} = 0.004$$

For an error of 2 amp in a reading of 100 amp the relative error would be

$$E_r = \frac{E_a}{X_m} = \tfrac{2}{100} = 0.02$$

percentage error

The *percentage error* is the relative error expressed as a percentage; thus to obtain the percentage error we multiply the relative error by 100. The percentage error E_p can be expressed as

$$E_p = E_r \times 100 = \frac{E_a}{X_m} \times 100 \qquad\qquad \textbf{2-3}$$

For the same example the percentage errors would be

$$E_p = E_r \times 100 = 0.004 \times 100 = 0.4 \text{ percent}$$

for the 500-amp circuit and

$$E_p = E_r \times 100 = 0.02 \times 100 = 2.0 \text{ percent}$$

for the 100-amp circuit.

ERROR ∝ ACCURACY
DISCREPANCY ∝ PRECISION

discrepancy

The difference between two or more measurements of the same quantity is called a *discrepancy*. This difference is not strictly an error. An error is the difference between a measured value and the true or best value; hence it is a function of accuracy. A discrepancy, which is the difference between one measured value and another, is a function of precision. The more sensitive the measuring instrument, the more discrepancies it will reveal. For example, suppose a skilled machinist makes successive measurements of a 2-in. part with a micrometer and with a steel ruler, as shown in Fig. 2-1. With the micrometer he may obtain values of 2.003, 2.001, 2.004, 2.002, and 2.002 in., indicating some discrepancy, whereas with a steel ruler graduated to hundredths of an inch he

figure *2-1   Measurement with a micrometer and with a steel ruler*

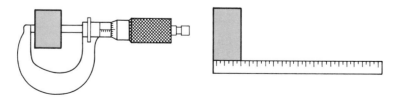

may obtain five successive values of 2.00 in., indicating no discrepancy. Thus it is not the measurer's aim to make measurements that show no discrepancy or to have the errors as small as possible, but rather to make measurements that show a small enough *range* of discrepancies and errors to enable him to draw conclusions or make statistical inferences from the measured values.

2-2   MATHEMATICAL ERRORS

Any measurement is a comparison of the unknown quantity with some type of measuring device and ultimately entails reading a value from some type of graduated scale. No matter how finely graduated a scale is, the final digit read from it must be an estimate of the distance between the smallest gradations. Consider the typical automobile speedometer shown in Fig. 2-2. The smallest gradation is 5 mph, and the needle rests somewhere between 25 and 30 mph. On closer observation we might estimate 27 mph, but any further refinement of this reading, say 27.3 mph, would be useless with the scale divisions shown.

The number of significant figures in a measurement is determined by the gradation of the scale. It is customary to read any fractional part of the smallest marked gradation as an additional full increment. Anyone dealing with measurements must be familiar with such conventions so that subsequent arithmetic operations

figure 2-2   An automobile speedometer

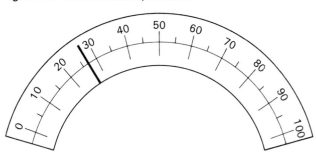

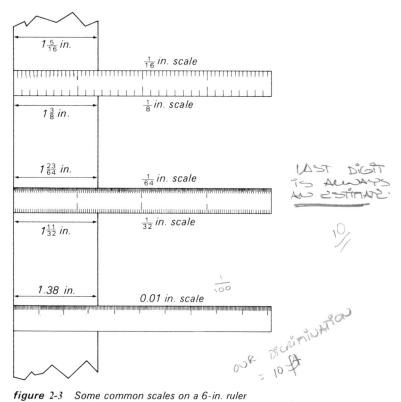

figure 2-3   Some common scales on a 6-in. ruler

and calculations are consistent with the measured values. Significant figures are discussed in Appendix B and should be reviewed at this point.

The magnitude of the smallest graduation on the readout scale is its *discrimination*. Hence the discrimination of the speedometer in Fig. 2-2 would be 5 mph.

Some of the common scales on an ordinary 6-in. steel ruler are shown in Fig. 2-3. Note that the same distance shows slightly different readings on each of the scales. Note also that regardless of how finely graduated the scale is, the last digit read from it must be an estimate.

2-3 PHYSICAL ERRORS

In addition to inherent and mathematical errors, all measurements are subject to certain physical errors. It is customary to group these in three categories.*

instrumental errors

Instrumental errors are those that result from imperfections in the measuring equipment itself. No measuring instrument can be made completely free of all imperfection, but these faults may be augmented by poor design or construction, faulty adjustment or calibration, or a combination of these. In addition to initial faults such as failure to correct for the zero reading, misaligned moving parts, graduation errors in scales, electric leakage, and poor optics, further inaccuracies are introduced by wear from normal use. Adjustment and calibration errors can be minimized by periodic checking and recalibration of the instrument.

personal or human errors

The observation of any measurement is limited by the range of human perception. Two persons reading the same needle on a meter will probably record slightly different values. Moreover, in spite of all precautions, there will be some error in the readings made by the most careful and experienced observer; some people consistently read scales high or low. Of course, if the scale is misread, or if it is read correctly and the wrong value is recorded, this is a mistake, not a personal error.

natural errors

Natural errors are those due to variations in natural phenomena, which in turn influence the accuracy of the measuring device or the capacity of the measurer to observe the result. Some of these phenomena are temperature, pressure, humidity, refraction, gravity,

*R. C. Brinker and W. C. Taylor, "Elementary Surveying," 4th ed., International Textbook Company, Scranton, Pa., 1962. R. E. Davis, F. S. Foote, and J. W. Kelly, "Surveying: Theory and Practice," 5th ed., McGraw-Hill Book Company, New York, 1966.

wind, and magnetic forces. The classic example involves the length of a steel measuring tape, which will increase or decrease with temperature, thus introducing an error into the readings.

2-4 SYSTEMATIC AND RANDOM ERRORS

In addition to the previous classification, errors may be grouped in two somewhat broader categories.

systematic or cumulative errors

A systematic error is one that has or tends to have the same magnitude and algebraic sign for a given set of conditions and follows some known mathematical or physical principle. Such errors are often constant owing to misadjustment of the measuring device or personal bias of the observer. Because they have the same algebraic sign, they tend to accumulate and hence are also known as cumulative errors.

If the conditions are specified, such errors may be evaluated and corrected for. Consider the systematic error of expansion or contraction introduced in a 100-ft surveyor's steel tape by temperature changes. When the coefficient of thermal expansion is known for a linear measuring instrument, the correction or adjustment of distances measured under conditions other than standard can be calculated by the relation

$$C_T = \text{Coefficient of thermal expansion} \times L(T - T_0) \qquad \textbf{2-4}$$

where C_T = correction for temperature
L = measured length
T = temperature in degrees Fahrenheit at which the measurements are taken
T_0 = temperature in degrees Fahrenheit at which the tape was standardized, usually 68°F.

example 2-1 A 100-ft steel surveyor's tape was used to measure the distance between two points on a flat level surface when the temperature was observed to be 92°F.

The tape had previously been standardized and was found to be 100.00 ft at 68°F. If the measured distance was recorded as 385.23 ft, what would be a more accurate value after correction for temperature effects? The coefficient of thermal expansion for steel is 0.0000065 ft/ft per F°. In other words, for every degree change in temperature the piece of steel will expand or contract 0.0000065 ft for every foot of length. This is commonly expressed as 0.0000065 per °F.

Substituting the value of the coefficient in Eq. 2-4, we have

$$C_T = 0.0000065 \times L(T - T_0)$$
$$= 0.0000065 \times 385.23\,(92 - 68) = 0.06 \text{ ft}$$

The tape is longer at the higher temperature, and so the measured reading is too small. Hence the correction C_T must be added to the measured length L. The corrected length is

$$385.23 + 0.06 = 385.29 \text{ ft}$$

example 2-2   The magnitude of an electric current in a circuit is measured by an ammeter. A meter reading of 25.8 amp is observed and recorded. Subsequently it is noted that the pointer indicates 0.2 amp of current when the device is not connected to the circuit. Determine a corrected current reading.

Since the ammeter indicated 0.2 amp when there is no current flowing, all the readings must be 0.2 amp too great. Hence we subtract the 0.2 from the observed reading to find a corrected reading of $25.8 - 0.2 = 25.6$ amp.

From these two examples we have the following rule for correcting systematic errors when *measuring* a quantity:

1   If a systematic error causes the measuring device to be too long, the measured quantity will be too small; hence the correction must be added, as shown in Fig. 2-4.

2   If a systematic error causes the measuring device to be

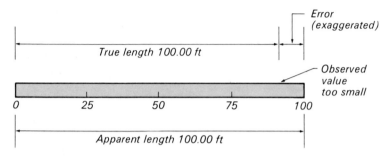

figure 2-4 *Correction when the measuring device is too long*

too short, the measured quantity will be too great; hence the correction must be subtracted, as shown in Fig. 2-5.

In *laying out* a quantity the rules are reversed:

1 If a systematic error causes the measuring device to be too long, the quantity laid out will be too great, and the correction must be subtracted.
2 If a systematic error causes the measuring device to be too short, the quantity laid out will be too small, and the correction must be added.

accidental or random errors

Accidental errors are unavoidable human errors of observation that occur in making repeated measurements. These random errors vary in magnitude and may be either positive or negative on

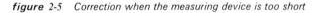

figure 2-5 *Correction when the measuring device is too short*

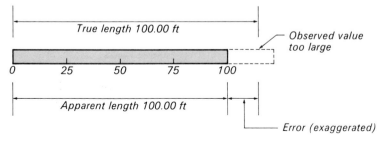

the basis of chance alone. Since they are random in either direction, it follows that they tend to compensate one another; hence they are frequently referred to as compensating errors. Their presence can be detected by the occurrence of discrepancies in a series of measurements made with the same measuring device by the same observer.

It is generally difficult to distinguish between accidental and systematic errors, and it is likely that many observational errors are a combination of both. However, after the systematic errors have been reduced or essentially eliminated, theoretically the accidental errors in any series of measurements follow the laws of probability. In addition, they submit to a statistical analysis which may have any of the following basic objectives:

1 Determination of the best or most probable value
2 Specifying the reliability of the best value
3 Prediction of the probability with which the next measurement would have a particular value
4 Selection of the best technique and most economical equipment in a particular case

We will devote the next several chapters of this text to an introduction into the concepts of probability and statistics as they relate to measurement and error theory.

SUMMARY

Whatever the nature of the measurement, the exact information desired is never obtained because all measurements contain inherent errors. The absolute error E_a of any measurement is the difference between the measured value X_m and the true or accepted value X_t. The absolute error divided by the measured value gives the relative error E_r; expressed as a percentage, it is known as the percentage error E_p. We call the difference between two or more measured values of the same quantity a discrepancy.

In addition to these inherent errors, any measurement contains a mathematical error introduced by the final significant figure. The reading of measurements from graduated scales determines the number of significant figures in the result; this includes all the digits read from the graduated scale plus a final digit, which is always estimated. The magnitude of the smallest division on the readout scale is the scale discrimination.

Physical errors in measurement are classified as personal or human errors, which are caused by the limitations of the human senses; instrumental errors, which result from the inherent imperfections in the equipment; and natural errors, which are due to variations in natural phenomena.

Errors may also be classified as systematic or accidental. Systematic errors, which follow some known mathematical or physical principle, tend to have the same algebraic sign for a given set of conditions and hence are cumulative. Accidental errors are random and may be either positive or negative on the basis of chance alone; hence they tend to compensate each other in any given set of measurements.

PROBLEMS

2-1 A 100-ft steel tape is standardized at 68°F. If the coefficient of thermal expansion is 0.0000065 per F° what is its corrected length to the nearest hundredth of a foot at 35°F?

2-2 The length of a line on a smooth horizontal surface is measured with a 50-ft metallic tape and found to be 835.12 ft when the temperature is 45°F. If the tape was standardized at 68°F and had a coefficient of thermal expansion of 0.0000065 per F°, what is the corrected length of the line to the nearest hundredth of a foot?

2-3 A 100-m distance is to be laid out for a track meet. A 100-ft steel tape is used; when the tape is compared with the standard, it is found to be 0.04 ft too short. What distance, to the nearest hundredth of a foot, should be laid out? One meter is equal to 3.2808 ft.

2-4 The corners of a new building must be laid out as accurately as possible with a 50-ft tape; the actual length of the tape is known to be 50.04 ft. The dimensions are to be 60.00 by 95.00 ft. Compute the measurements that need to be made to the nearest hundredth of a foot.

2-5 What is another name for systematic errors?

2-6 What is another name for accidental errors?

2-7 A distance of 94.7 ft is measured and is believed to be correct to the nearest 0.3 ft. What are the absolute, relative, and percentage errors in the measurement?

2-8 Frequently a measurement is shown as a number and an allowable percentage error. For a measurement of a resistance of 15.6 ohms $\pm$ 0.5 percent, determine the absolute and relative errors.

2-9 In industry the total variation permitted in the manufacture of a part is called the *tolerance*. The tolerance for the diameter of a certain cylindrical shaft is expressed as 1.250 in. ± 0.5 percent. If several shafts selected at random from the production are found to have the following measurements, which ones are not acceptable?

1.253	1.252	1.257	1.249	1.248
1.243	1.251	1.252	1.256	1.250

2-10 A manufacturer desires to maintain the quality of his product by establishing maximum and minimum dimensions for a certain critical component at 0.625 $\pm$ 0.005 in. Determine the absolute error, the relative error, and the percentage error allowed under these specifications.

2-11 Two experimenters independently measured the specific gravity of benzene at 32°F. Experimenter A obtained a value of 0.874 and experimenter B a value of 0.884. If the accepted value is 0.879, which experimenter had the largest absolute error, relative error, and percentage error?

2-12 A property line is measured by a surveyor and is found to be 249.8 ft. If the distance is correct to the nearest 0.5 ft, what is the percentage error?

2-13 A triangular pattern is laid out as shown with a steel scale that was thought to be exactly 3 ft long. Subsequently it is found that the steel scale was actually 2.97 ft long. What were the actual pattern dimensions?

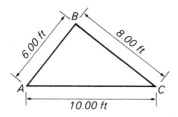

2-14 A dial gage is used to measure the pressure in a vessel. The pivot is not exactly centered, and as a result the readings are subject to a systematic error. By experiment it is determined that this imperfection makes the readings too large, with the magnitude of the error varying linearly from 1.0 psi for a dial reading of zero to 4.0 psi for a dial reading of 150 psi. What would be the value of the pressure for each of the following dial readings?

a	150	*d*	1
b	100	*e*	75
c	50	*f*	125

2-15 A 300-ft steel tape is compared with a standard and is found to be 0.27 ft too long. Compute the error likely in making a measurement of 1,300.00 ft.

2-16 A line 1 mile long is measured with a steel tape. What error will be introduced if the actual temperature of the tape is 10°F above the temperature at which it was standardized?

2-17 A meter stick is used to measure a distance of 48 cm. If it is read to the nearest millimeter, what is the absolute error and relative error?

2-18 A 440-yd straightway track is to be laid out with a 100-ft tape that is known to be 99.75 ft long. What measurement to the nearest hundredth of a foot should be made with this tape?

2-19 A 5-ft steel scale is actually 5 ft $\frac{3}{16}$ in. long at 68°F. What distance to the nearest sixteenth of an inch should be laid out with this scale to obtain a correct length of 25 ft $4\frac{1}{2}$ in. at 30°F.?

2-20 Round off each of the following numbers to three significant figures:

a	4.326	*e*	0.4075
b	0.93549	*f*	9.33499
c	70.05×10^{-3}	*g*	2.78501
d	3.8451	*h*	π

2-21 Indicate the number of significant figures in each of the following measurements:

a	9.54	*g*	5,050,000	*m*	1.340
b	0.004390	*h*	0.040	*n*	40,000
c	1.53×10^5	*i*	2.745×10^5	*o·*	13.050
d	27,000	*j*	0.4003	*p*	1.750×10^2
e	0.00053	*k*	2.90	*q*	10
f	1.7×10^8	*l*	40093	*r*	5.90540

2-22 Round off each of the following measurements, all of which are in inches to the indicated accuracy:

a 59.7 to the nearest unit
b 3.954 to the nearest hundredth
c 0.0975 to the nearest thousandth
d 0.00354 to two significant figures
e 14.50001 to the nearest unit

 f   47567 to three significant figures
 g   0.000765 to one significant figure
 h   35,499 to the nearest thousand
 i   35,500 to the nearest thousand
 j   478 to the nearest hundred

2-23   The following measurements are in centimeters:

 15.45   6.95   1.25   3.85   12.4

 a   Add them without regard to significant figures
 b   Add them according to the addition rule for significant figures
 c   Add them by first rounding to the nearest tenth in accordance with proper procedure
 d   Compare the results

2-24   For each of the following measurements what is the maximum error?

 a   494.74 miles
 b   0.008500 cm
 c 5.373×10^5 microns

2-25   The measurements are in feet:

 5.19352   14.33   2.2   8.934   5.7347

 a   Add them without regard to significant figures
 b   Add them according to the addition rule for significant figures
 c   Add them by rounding first but keeping one more significant figure than that in the value with the least significant figure
 d   Compare the results

2-26   Add the following measurements and then express the answer to the correct number of significant figures:

a	12.3457	*b*	0.003751
	3.21		1.234
	0.00413		5.691
	7.34		6.35
	5.2		0.094

2-27 Subtract the following measurements and then express the answer to the correct number of significant figures:

    a 75,075 − 4,375.32

    b 0.08334 − 0.0041

    c 3,565.07 − 0.0004

    d 0.000934 − 0.02

2-28 Multiply the following measurements and then express the answer to the correct number of significant figures:

    a. 5,475 × 1.07

    b 141.3 × 5.2

    c $1.93 \times 10^6 \times 0.3$

2-29 Divide the following measurements and then express the answer to the correct number of significant figures:

    a $\dfrac{4,735}{0.30}$

    b $\dfrac{0.009437}{1.37}$

    c $\dfrac{0.008350}{4,175}$

2-30 The corners for a horizontal rectangular jig must be laid out as accurately as possible with a 50-ft metal tape which is found to be

50.00 ft at 68°F. If the dimensions of the jig are to be 125.00 by 157.50 ft, compute the dimensions to the nearest hundredth of a foot needed for the layout if the temperature during the work is 40°F. The coefficient of thermal expansion of the metal is 0.0000065 per °F.

three

concepts of
probability

In our study of measurements we strive to observe data by means of refined techniques and to employ careful analysis so that we may be reasonably assured of a degree of accuracy in our results. The principles underlying our methods are part of the study of mathematical probability and statistics. Much of our discussion of these mathematical concepts has been kept at an elementary level. For example, to a statistician the terms *event* and *outcome* have different meanings. However, in this chapter we shall use these terms merely to refer to the elements that can be observed from a game of chance or an experiment, such as observing a three in the toss of a single die or a head in the toss of a single coin. In a broad sense events may include specified groupings of these outcomes, such as the even or odd numbers in the toss of a single die.

Let us begin by defining the term *probability*. We will define probability as the ratio of successful outcomes to all possible outcomes,

$$P = \frac{N}{N_T} \hspace{4cm} \textbf{3-1}$$

where N is the number of successes and N_T is the number of tries. A probability of 1 indicates an absolute certainty and a probability of 0 an impossibility (many times we assign a zero probability to events that are improbable). Later, when we introduce the concepts of statistics, we will refine this definition.

A few examples will clarify this definition. Since the theory of probability developed from analytical studies of games of chance, let us consider examples from these games. One of the most basic examples is a *fair die*, an evenly balanced cube whose six sides are numbered. When this die is rolled a large number of times, the probability of obtaining a one will approach $\frac{1}{6}$. Our definition of probability would indicate this to be the correct value, as there is only one way to be successful out of the six possible outcomes.

Let us select a slightly more complicated example, the inference of probability. Suppose two observers are watching a dealer;

the dealer is about to turn a card from the top of the deck. Before he turns the card someone asks, "What is the probability that the card will be a spade?" Observer 1, who has gotten a brief glimpse of the card, knows that it is black, and so he answers, "One-half." Observer 2, who has not seen the card at all, answers, "One-quarter." Which of these answers is correct? Actually, both observers have answered to the best of their knowledge. In this case observer 1 had more knowledge than observer 2, and it would be wrong for him to neglect it in his answer. This point is important in dealing with engineering measurements, where use of less than the best available evidence will yield marginal results.

In most cases involving engineering measurements the data we observe are controlled by one of several probability distributions; a few of these will be discussed later. It will be our task to observe samples and determine the probability distribution that best defines the behavior of our data. We will attempt to infer the characteristics of this distribution by the mathematical techniques discussed in subsequent chapters. First let us carefully define and discuss some terms commonly used in probability theory and then introduce some important elementary probability laws.

3-2 MUTUALLY EXCLUSIVE EVENTS

If two or more events are such that not more than one of them can occur in a single trial, then the events are said to be *mutually exclusive*. For example, in one draw from a deck, the two events of drawing both an ace and a king are mutually exclusive. In the single throw of one die, the events of getting both a two and a three are mutually exclusive. However, the two events of picking a seven and a spade in a single draw are not mutually exclusive, because both events would occur if we happen to draw the seven of spades.

3-3 INDEPENDENT AND DEPENDENT EVENTS

An event is said to be *independent* if the probability of its occurrence is not influenced by the outcome of other events. For example, if a single die is thrown twice, the occurrence of a three on the first throw and a six on the second throw are independent events, because the outcome of the first event in no way affects the outcome of the second. If two cards are drawn from a deck, an ace on the first draw and a king on the second draw are independent events if the first card is replaced before the second is drawn. If the occurrence of one event is influenced by the outcome of some other event, then the events are *dependent*. The probabilities of drawing an ace and a king in two successive draws from a deck are dependent if the draw is made without replacement. Holding out the ace obtained on the first draw increases the probability of drawing a king on the second, because the number of remaining cards is reduced by one, while the number of kings remain the same. We will study this principle further in Chapter Three.

3-4 ADDITION LAW OF PROBABILITY

mutually exclusive events

The probability of occurrence of all of several mutually exclusive events is the sum of the separate probabilities. Thus if P_1, P_2, P_3, ..., P_n are the separate probabilities of n mutually exclusive events, the probability P that all these events will occur is

$$P = P_1 + P_2 + P_3 + \cdots + P_n \qquad\qquad 3\text{-}2$$

It should be noted that the sum of all probabilities of all possible outcomes is always equal to 1.

example *3-1* What is the probability of drawing an ace or a king in a single draw from a deck?

The probability of an ace is

$$P(A) = \tfrac{4}{52} = \tfrac{1}{13}$$

and the probability of a king is

$$P(K) = \tfrac{4}{52} = \tfrac{1}{13}$$

Hence, from Eq. 3-2, the probability of drawing an ace or a king is

$$P(A + K) = \tfrac{1}{13} + \tfrac{1}{13} = \tfrac{2}{13}$$

example 3-2   What is the probability of drawing an ace, or a king, or a queen in a single draw?

The probability of each of these events is

$$P(A) = \tfrac{1}{13} \qquad P(K) = \tfrac{1}{13} \qquad P(Q) = \tfrac{1}{13}$$

Hence the probability of any of the three is

$$P(A + K + Q) = \tfrac{1}{13} + \tfrac{1}{13} + \tfrac{1}{13} = \tfrac{3}{13}$$

events not mutually exclusive

The probability of events that are *not* mutually exclusive is computed differently, because they can all occur simultaneously. Thus if A and B denote two events that are not mutually exclusive, then the probability of obtaining event A or event B or both is given as

$$P(A + B) = P(A) + P(B) - P(AB) \qquad\qquad 3\text{-}3$$

That is, the probability of event A or event B or both equals the sum of the separate probabilities minus the probability that both events will occur. We will define this mathematical notation more completely later. Note that Eq. 3-2 is really a special case of Eq. 3-3, where the last term, $P(AB)$, equals 0, since for mutually exclusive events it is impossible for both A and B to occur simultaneously.

It should be pointed out that although the notation we use here is that used in recent engineering literature, there is no established convention in this field of mathematics. Hence the following equivalent forms, among others, appear in mathematical works:

$$P(AB) \equiv P(A \cap B) \equiv P(A \wedge B) \equiv P(A \text{ and } B)$$

$$P(A + B) \equiv P(A \cup B) \equiv P(A \wedge B) \equiv P(A \text{ or } B)$$

example 3-3   What is the probability of drawing either a seven or a spade or both in a single draw?

The probability of drawing a seven is

$P(7) = \frac{4}{52}$

and the probability of drawing a spade is

$P(S) = \frac{13}{52}$

Thus the probability of drawing the seven of spades is

$P(7S) = \frac{1}{52}$

From Eq. 3-3,

$P(A + B) = P(A) + P(B) - P(AB)$

Therefore

$P(7 + S) = P(7) + P(S) - P(7S)$

$$= \frac{4}{52} + \frac{13}{52} - \frac{1}{52} = \frac{17}{52} - \frac{1}{52} = \frac{16}{52} = \frac{4}{13}$$

3-5 MULTIPLICATION LAW OF PROBABILITY

independent events

If $P_1, P_2, P_3, \ldots, P_n$ are the probabilities of n independent events, the probability P that all of these events will occur in a trial is

$$P = P_1 P_2 P_3 \ldots P_n \qquad\qquad 3\text{-}4$$

example 3-4 Compute the probability of drawing first an ace and then a king from a deck if the first card drawn is replaced before the second one is drawn.

The probability of drawing an ace is

$P(A) = \frac{1}{13}$

and the probability of drawing a king is

$P(K) = \frac{1}{13}$

Then, from Eq. 3-4, the probability of drawing an ace and a king in successive draws is

$$P(AK) = P(A)P(K) = \tfrac{1}{13} \times \tfrac{1}{13} = \tfrac{1}{169}$$

since the events are independent.

example *3-5*   What is the probability of obtaining three heads if three coins are tossed just once?

The probability of a head on each coin is

$$P(H) = \tfrac{1}{2}$$

Thus probability of obtaining three heads in a single toss of three coins is

$$P(HHH) = P(H)P(H)P(H) = \tfrac{1}{2} \times \tfrac{1}{2} \times \tfrac{1}{2} = \tfrac{1}{8}$$

dependent events

Suppose P_1 is the probability of the first of n dependent events and P_2', P_3', and so on are the probabilities of subsequent events *provided* the first event occurs. Then the probability P that all subsequent events will occur in the specified order is

$$P = P_1 P_2' P_3' \ldots P_n' \qquad\qquad 3\text{-}5$$

Note that each P' probability depends on the occurrence of the preceding events. This will be explained later when we discuss conditional probability.

example *3-6*   What is the probability of drawing first an ace and then a king if the cards are drawn without replacement?

The probability of drawing an ace on the first card is

$$P(A) = \tfrac{1}{13}$$

and the probability of drawing a king on the second card is

$$P(K) = \tfrac{4}{51}$$

Then, from Eq. 3-5, the probability of drawing first an ace and then a king is

$$P(AK) = P(A)P(K) = \tfrac{1}{13} \times \tfrac{4}{51} = \tfrac{4}{663}$$

3-6 EXCLUDED EVENTS

Let us suppose that N_B is the number of times event B occurs and N_T is the number of total possible outcomes. Then the probability that event B will occur is

$$P(B) = \frac{N_B}{N_T}$$

If we define $\bar{B}$ as any event *except* B—that is as *not* B—then the probability that event B will *not* occur is

$$P(\bar{B}) = \frac{N_T - N_B}{N_T}$$

It follows that

$$P(B) + P(\bar{B}) = 1 \qquad\qquad\qquad \textbf{3-6}$$

3-7 VENN DIAGRAMS

One of the easiest ways to illustrate the concepts of probability is by means of a *Venn diagram*, which is a graphic representation of the number of outcomes of a particular set of data. In the diagram shown in Fig. 3-1, the large outside area includes all possible outcomes and is labled *S*. Area *S* is defined as the *sample space*. There

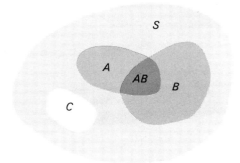

figure *3-1   A Venn diagram*

is one area to represent event A, one for event B, and one for event C. Note that event C is completely separate from events A and B, but events A and B have a common area. The common area represents those events which are both A and B. Thus this Venn diagram shows that events A and C and events B and C are mutually exclusive and that A and B are not.

mutually exclusive events

Let us apply the Venn diagram to a more complicated example. In Fig. 3-2 the total sample area includes all students at a large university. One area inside the sample area represents engineering students, which we will call event A; a second area represents male students, event B; and another area represents language students, event C. Note that engineering students and language students are separate categories; for the sake of discussion here, there are no engineering students who are also studying language. However, the male students include some engineering and some language students. The fact that males compromise a portion of each of these categories is apparent from the Venn diagram.

We have defined two items as being mutually exclusive when the occurrence of one precludes the occurrence of the other. For example, if a student falls in the category of males he cannot also fall in the category of females; thus these events are mutually

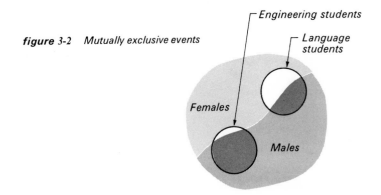

figure 3-2   *Mutually exclusive events*

Engineering students

Language students

Females

Males

exclusive. Let us assume, for the sake of our example, that 50 percent of the student body are males. Let us also assume that 50 percent of the language students are males and 90 percent of the engineers are males. Now consider our previous explanation of independent events. The knowledge that an individual is a language student or a student at a large university in no way influences the probability that a student is a male. Both categories are half males and half females; therefore the event that an individual is a language student or a student at the university gives no information about whether the student is a male. However, the knowledge that a student is an engineer does have a connection; since 90 percent of the engineering students are male, the fact that the student is an engineer indicates a 90 percent probability that the student is also a male. Note that if two events are mutually exclusive they cannot be independent, since the occurrence of the first event makes the probability of the second event zero. This concept will be expanded later when we discuss conditional probability.

Consider the determination of probability in terms of mutually exclusive events. In Fig. 3-3 the events are male and female, and their sum is the total population. If we let B denote males and $\bar{B}$ denote females, then, from Eq. 3-6, the total population is

$$N_T = N_M + N_F$$

the intersection of events

The probability of the simultaneous occurrence of events A and B, defined as the *intersection* of A and B, is denoted as $P(AB)$. Consider the Venn diagram in Fig. 3-4, where event A is being an engineering student, event B is being a male, and $P(AB)$ is the probability of being a male engineering student. We see that the probability of the intersection of events A and B—that the student will be both a male and an engineering student—is

$$P(AB) = \frac{N_{ME}}{N_T} \qquad\qquad 3\text{-}7$$

where N_{ME} is the number of male engineering students and N_T is the total student population.

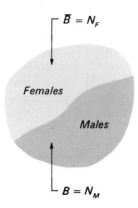

figure 3-3   Determining total population

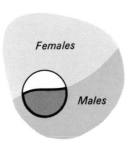

figure 3-4   Probability of the intersection of events

figure 3-5   Probability of the union of events

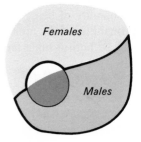

the union of events

The probability of events A or B or both, defined as the *union* of A or B, is denoted as $P(A + B)$. Consider the Venn diagram in Fig. 3-5, where again event A is being an engineering student and event B is being a male. The probability of the union of A or B is thus the probability that a student will be either a male or an engineering student or both,

$$P(A + B) = 1 - P(\overline{A + B}) = 1 - \frac{N_F - N_{FE}}{N_T} \qquad \textbf{3-8}$$

where $N_F - N_{FE}$ is the number of nonengineering females. The expression $P(\overline{A + B})$ derives directly from $P(A) + P(\overline{A}) = 1$ and is used here because it is easier to count the female engineering students than it is to count students in the category $A + B$. This will be emphasized shortly.

3-8 CONDITIONAL PROBABILITY

Let us now introduce some notation for the concept of *conditional probability*. The probability of event B given that event C has occurred is written mathematically as $P(B|C)$. The conditional probability that a student is male given that he is a language student, $P(\text{male}|\text{language student})$, is shown in Fig. 3-6. Suppose that event B is being a male and event C is being a language student. Then this probability is

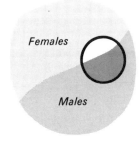

Females

Males

figure *3-6   Conditional probability*

$$P(B|C) = \frac{P(BC)}{P(C)} \qquad\qquad\qquad 3\text{-}9$$

where $P(BC)$ is the number of male language majors and $P(C)$ is the number of language majors. Note that here the sample size is the number of language students rather than the total student population.

Equation 3-9 is the *general form* for conditional probability. In terms of two arbitrary events we may rewrite it as

$$P(A|B) = \frac{P(AB)}{P(B)} \qquad \text{if } P(B) \neq 0 \qquad\qquad 3\text{-}10$$

In Eq. 3-5 we used the notation P' for conditional probability; it is more acceptable to write this instead as $P(A|B)$.

At this point we will return to the concept of independence and show its relationship to conditional probability. Rewriting Eq. 3-10 yields the probability of intersection of A and B,

$$P(AB) = P(A|B)P(B) \qquad\qquad\qquad 3\text{-}11$$

We saw in Eq. 3-4 that for independent events the probability of the intersection of A and B would be stated as

$$P(AB) = P(A)P(B)$$

This is actually a special case of Eq. 3-11 if $P(A) = P(A|B)$. Therefore Eq. 3-11 is used to evaluate the intersection of two events regardless of independence, while Eq. 3-4 is used for independent events only. This provides us with a method of determining independence, since two events are independent if $P(A) = P(A|B)$. For example, in our discussion of Fig. 3-2 we saw that with the assumptions $P(B|C) = 0.50$ and $P(B) = 0.50$, being a language student was independent of being a student at large in determining whether an individual student was a male. However, since we assumed for engineering students that $P(B|A) = 0.90$, and $P(B|A) \neq P(B)$, these two events were dependent.

Regarding the dependence of mutually exclusive events, note that independence implies $P(A|B) = P(A)$, while mutually exclusive events imply $P(A|B) = 0$.

In defining the probability of the union of two events in Eq. 3-8 we used the form that probability is 1 minus the probability that the union did not occur. Let us now express this relation in the more conventional form of Eq. 3-3, as illustrated in Fig. 3-7,

$$P(A + B) = P(A) + P(B) - P(AB)$$

Note that in adding $P(A)$ to $P(B)$ we have included the intersection of AB twice; hence we must subtract it out once.

This concept is readily expanded to

$$P(D + E + F) = P(D) + P(E) + P(F) - P(DE)$$
$$- P(DF) - P(EF) + P(DEF) \quad \textbf{3-12}$$

as shown by the Venn diagram in Fig. 3-8. Here we have added $P(DEF)$ three times and subtracted out the shaded area $P(DEF)$

figure *3-7   Union of two events*

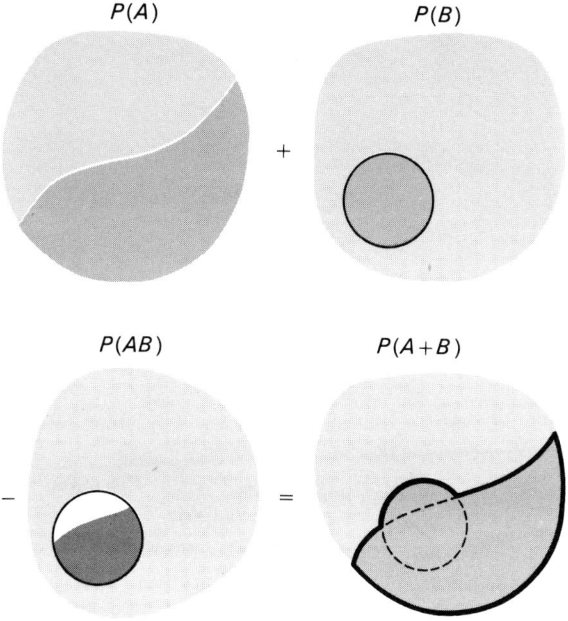

$P(A)$ $P(B)$

$+$

$P(AB)$ $P(A+B)$

$-$ $=$

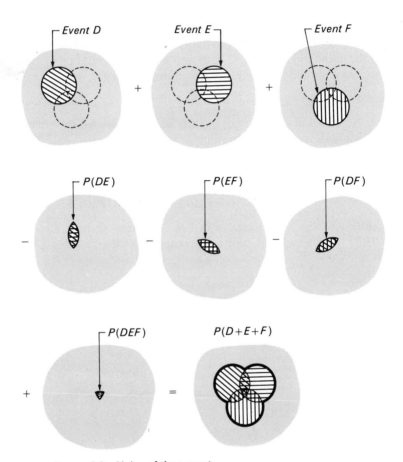

figure 3-8   *Union of three events*

three times; hence we must add it back in. The subtraction takes place in the terms $-P(DE)$ $-P(DF)$ $-P(EF)$, and the area was originally included in the terms $P(D) + P(E) + P(F)$. We are thus left with the task of accounting for the shaded area $P(DEF)$ as a separate term. Since each term in Eq. 3-12 represents a ratio with respect to our chosen population, it is apparent that we need a

$$P = \frac{N}{N_T}$$ where $N = \#$ of success
$N_i = \#$ of tries

great deal of information about the population to calculate this type of probability.

Let us consider a few examples to illustrate our definitions.

example 3-7 A large trucking firm which operates both gasoline and diesel trucks kept yearly records on engine overhauls for its fleet. Below is a tabulation of the number of miles before overhaul for each type of vehicle. What is the probability that an engine will exceed 50,000 miles prior to overhaul?

There are two basic approaches to this problem. The first and most straightforward approach is to find N_A, the number of engines that exceeded 50,000 miles before overhaul, and divide it by N_T, the total number of engines in this limited population. Thus

$$P(A) = \frac{N_A}{N_T} = \frac{150 + 650}{1,000} = 0.8$$

The second approach employs the concept that $P(A) = 1 - P(\overline{A})$. We therefore find N_A, the number of engines requiring overhaul prior to 50,000 miles, and use that value in our calculations. Thus

$$P(A) = 1 - \frac{200}{1,000} = 1.0 - 0.2 = 0.8$$

What is the probability that an engine will exceed 100,000 miles? What effect does the engine type have on this probability?

Miles \ Vehicle	Gasoline	Diesel	Total
100,001 and over	50	100	150
50,001–100,000	300	350	650
0–50,000	150	50	200
Total	500	500	1,000

Once again we can answer the first question by means of the simple concept of probability:

$$P(A) = \frac{N_A}{N_T} = \frac{150}{1,000} = 0.15$$

The second question adds conditions to the problem, and we enter the case of conditional probability, $P(A|B) = P(AB)/P(B)$. That is, in terms of the problem at hand: What is the probability that an engine will exceed 100,000 miles prior to overhaul given the engine is gasoline or diesel? Solving for the gasoline case gives

$$P(A|B) = \frac{\frac{50}{1,000}}{\frac{500}{1,000}} = 0.1$$

The exact equation for $P(AB)$ and $P(B)$ shows how the total sample size cancels out and the problem is reduced to a comparison of gasoline engines exceeding 100,000 miles to the total number of gasoline engines. The same procedure applied for the diesel engines yields a probability of 0.2.

example 3-8   Consider a single roll of two fair dice. All the possible combinations are shown below. To simplify our analysis, suppose that one die is white and the other is black. What is the probability of rolling a seven?

First we must realize what it is that we are trying to count; here N_A becomes the number of ways to roll a seven and N_T the number of possible outcomes. Thus

Black ⟍ White	One	Two	Three	Four	Five	Six
One	2	3	4	5	6	7
Two	3	4	5	6	7	8
Three	4	5	6	7	8	9
Four	5	6	7	8	9	10
Five	6	7	8	9	10	11
Six	7	8	9	10	11	12

$$P(A) = \frac{N_A}{N_T} = \tfrac{6}{36} = \tfrac{1}{6}$$

What is the probability of rolling a six on the black die? What is the probability of a six on the black die, *given that the white die is a two*? Are the values on the two dice independent of each other?

The probability of rolling a two on the white die is $P(B) = \tfrac{1}{6}$ and the probability of a six on the black die is $P(A) = \tfrac{1}{6}$. Thus

$$P(A|B) = \frac{P(AB)}{P(B)} = \frac{\tfrac{1}{36}}{\tfrac{6}{36}} = \tfrac{1}{6}$$

Since the conditional probability $P(A|B)$ is the same as $P(A)$, the knowledge of what is on the white die in no way effects the probability for the black die; the events are independent.

What is the probability of a black six and a white two on the same roll?

We see from the table that there is one possible successful outcome in 36 tries; hence the probability is $\tfrac{1}{36}$, and the outcomes are dependent. This is also shown by the general equation, Eq. 3-11,

$$P(AB) = P(A|B)\,P(B)$$

where A is the event of obtaining a black six and B is the event of getting a white two. Since $P(B) = \tfrac{1}{6}$ and $P(A|B) = \tfrac{1}{6}$,

$$P(AB) = \tfrac{1}{6} \times \tfrac{1}{6} = \tfrac{1}{36}$$

As a final example consider another method of enumerating possible outcomes.

example 3-9 Four fair coins are tossed sixteen times, with the outcomes for heads or tails as shown below. What is the probability of an outcome with only two heads?

Outcome Coin	1	2	3	4	5	6	7	8	9	10	11	12	13	14	15	16
1	H	H	H	H	H	H	H	H	T	T	T	T	T	T	T	T
2	H	H	H	H	T	T	T	T	H	H	H	H	T	T	T	T
3	H	H	T	T	H	H	T	T	H	H	T	T	H	H	T	T
4	H	T	H	T	H	T	H	T	H	T	H	T	H	T	H	T

Here we must count the number of outcomes with only two heads; there are six, outcomes 4, 6, 7, 10, 11, and 13. Thus

$$P(2H) = \frac{N_{2H}}{N_T} = \tfrac{6}{16} = \tfrac{3}{8}$$

What is the probability of two or more heads?

Here the question might better be worded: What is the probability of one or fewer heads? This form gives us fewer points to count, and we use Eq. 3-6,

$$P(A) + P(\overline{A}) = 1$$

or

$$P(A) = 1 - P(\overline{A})$$

Then the probability of two or more heads is

$$P(2H+) = 1 - P(1H-) = 1 - \tfrac{5}{16} = \tfrac{11}{16}$$

3-9   SIMPLE COUNTING TECHNIQUES

What happens when we are unable to use tables or graphics to show all possible outcomes of several different events? Are we to assume that we cannot evaluate their probabilities? In many cases we can employ very simple counting processes to determine the number of outcomes. There are times when counting processes fail and we may turn to more sophisticated methods, such as computer simulation; such methods are beyond the scope of this text, but will prove useful in advanced engineering applications.

We will use some of our examples from the previous section

to present these ideas. First, let us look at the problem of finding the total number of possible outcomes. Suppose we have two sets of outcomes from which to choose, and the first set has n_1 outcomes and the second has n_2; then there are $n_1 \times n_2$ ways of selecting first from set 1 and then from set 2. This can be seen from our example of two dice, where there are six outcomes for each die and 36 in the combined roll of both. This concept can be expanded when we are selecting from more than two sets, as in our last example of four coins, where the total number of outcomes is the product of the number of outcomes of each original set. We would say that with the four coins we should have $2 \times 2 \times 2 \times 2$, or 16 outcomes, which indeed we did. This can be expressed as follows:

$$N_T = n_1 n_2 \qquad \text{for two sets} \qquad \textbf{3-13}$$

$$N_T = n_1 n_2 n_3 \cdots n_k \qquad \text{for } k \text{ sets} \qquad \textbf{3-14}$$

example 3-10 Suppose you are selecting some breakfast cereal, milk, and sugar at your local market. There are 15 cereals to choose from, three brands of milk, and four brands of sugar. In how many different ways could you select your three purchases?

From Eq. 3-14 we have

$$N_T = 15 \times 3 \times 4 = 180$$

example 3-11 You belong to a club of 10 members in which any member may hold office. If the club selects first a president, then a vice-president, and finally a secretary treasurer, how many different ways can they be chosen from the membership?

The problem is to determine n_1, n_2, and n_3, the number of ways of selecting a president, a vice-president, and a secretary treasurer, respectively. Since the president is picked first, there are 10 ways of selection; the vice-president will be selected from the nine remaining and the secretary/treasurer from the last eight. Thus

$$N_T = 10 \times 9 \times 8 = 720$$

This last example leads to an important combinatorial method called *permutation.*

3-10 PERMUTATIONS

The number of ways of selecting a set of *r* elements from a set of *n* elements when the *order* of selection is important is referred to as the *permutation* of *r* elements from a set of *n* elements. Mathematically, this is expressed as

$$P_r^n = n(n - 1)(n - 2)(n - 3) \cdots (n - r + 1) \qquad \textbf{3-15}$$

where P_r^n is read as *the permutation of n elements taken r at a time.* This is also sometimes expressed as *nPr* or as *P(n,r).*

Here we are concerned not only with the identity of the items, but also with their arrangement. The meaning of Eq. 3-15 is intuitively apparent when we consider the meaning of *order.* We must first select from our *n* elements one to occupy the first position of a grouping of *r* elements; since we have *n* elements from which to select, we have *n* ways of selecting the element for this first position. Once an element has been selected, it is no longer available for any other position. Thus there are only *n* − 1 remaining elements to fill the second position and so on, down to *n* − *r* + 1 elements to fill the *r*th position. In Example 3-11 any of the members can be elected president; however, once he has been elected, the president is no longer available for another office, and therefore there is one fewer member to be considered for the position of vice-president.

It is customary to indicate permutation in *factorial* notation. The product

$$n(n - 1)(n - 2)(n - 3) \cdots 1$$

is called *factorial n* and is denoted as *n*! Thus factorial 6 would be evaluated as

$$6! = 6 \times 5 \times 4 \times 3 \times 2 \times 1 = 720$$

Factorial 7 times factorial 3 would be

$$7! \, 3! = (7 \times 6 \times 5 \times 4 \times 3 \times 2 \times 1)(3 \times 2 \times 1)$$
$$= 5{,}040 \times 6 = 30{,}240$$

Other examples are

$$\frac{8!}{4!} = \frac{(8 \times 7 \times 6 \times 5)4!}{4!} = 8 \times 7 \times 6 \times 5 = 1{,}680$$

$$\frac{9!}{3!4!} = \frac{(9 \times 8 \times 7 \times 6 \times 5)4!}{(3 \times 2 \times 1)4!} = 3 \times 4 \times 7 \times 6 \times 5$$
$$= 2{,}520$$

$$57! = 4.0527 \times 10^{76}$$

$$\frac{63!}{47!} = \frac{1.9826 \times 10^{87}}{2.5862 \times 10^{59}} = 7.66 \times 10^{27}$$

In these last two cases it is necessary to use the table in Appendix F. *By definition,* $0! = 1$.

Note that in some cases it is more convenient to rewrite the factorial notation in two parts. Thus

$$n! = \left[n(n-1)(n-2) \cdots (n - r + 1) \right]$$
$$\left[(n - r) \times \cdots \times 2 \times 1 \right]$$

and from Eq. 3-15,

$$n! = \left[P_r^{\,n} \right]\left[(n - r)! \right]$$

or

$$P_r^{\,n} = \frac{n!}{(n-r)!} \qquad\qquad\qquad \textbf{3-16}$$

example 3-12 How many different distinct ways can five transistors be selected from a group of 10?

From Eq. 3-16,

$$P_r^n = \frac{n!}{(n - r)!} = P_5^{10} = \frac{10!}{5!} = 10 \times 9 \times 8 \times 7 \times 6$$

$$= 30{,}240$$

It is important to note that the *order* of the transistors is considered significant.

3-11 COMBINATIONS

Another counting technique is employed to select r elements from a set of n elements when order is not important. This grouping, referred to as the *combination* of r elements from a set of n elements, is expressed mathematically as

$$C_r^n = \frac{n!}{(n - r)! r!} \qquad\qquad 3\text{-}17$$

The similarity to permutation is apparent. What we are saying is that of the r elements selected we assume only one combination of elements, since order is of no importance. Thus we must divide the number of outcomes obtained from our calculation of permutation by the number of ways the r elements can be arranged. Since by definition $0! = 1$,

$$C_r^n = \frac{P_r^n}{P_r^r} = \frac{n!/(n - r)!}{r!/0!} = \frac{n! 0!}{(n - r)! r!} = \frac{n!}{(n - r)! r!}$$

example 3-13 Returning to Example 3-12, suppose now that all the transistors are identical. How many ways are there to select five transistors from a group of 10?

Since we cannot tell the order, as the transistors are not distinguishable from each other, we use Eq. 3-17,

$$C_r^n = C_5^{10} = \frac{10!}{(10 - 5)! 5!} = \frac{10!}{5! 5!} = \frac{10 \times 9 \times 8 \times 7 \times 6}{5 \times 3 \times 4 \times 1 \times 2}$$

$$= 252$$

Note that the factorial 5 on the bottom has been arranged for easy cancellation.

example 3-14   Consider Example 3-9, where we flipped four fair coins. Without listing all the possible outcomes, calculate the probability of obtaining only two heads.

From Eq. 3-14,

$$N_T = n_1 n_2 n_3 n_4 = 2 \times 2 \times 2 \times 2 = 16 \text{ total outcomes}$$

We now need to calculate the number of ways of obtaining two heads from four coins that are identical. From Eq. 3-17 we have

$$C_2^4 = \frac{4!}{2!2!}$$

Thus the probability of obtaining two heads is

$$P(2H) = \frac{N_{2H}}{N_T} = \tfrac{6}{16} = \tfrac{3}{8}$$

example 3-15   If a certain radio has six identical tubes and you know that two of the six are bad, calculate the probability of randomly selecting two tubes and obtaining both the bad tubes.

The number of ways of selecting two tubes from six is given by Eq. 3-17 as

$$C_2^6 = \frac{6!}{4!2!} = \frac{6 \times 5}{2 \times 1} = 15 = N_T$$

The number of ways of selecting the two bad tubes out of two is given also by Eq. 3-17. Thus, if we call a bad tube event A,

$$C_2^2 = \frac{2!}{2!0!} = 1 = N_A$$

and

$$P(2A) = \frac{N_A}{N_T} = \tfrac{1}{15}$$

3-12 *HYPERGEOMETRIC AND BINOMIAL DISTRIBUTIONS*

Now that we have a basic understanding of probability, it is time to examine two basic probability distributions that enable us to evaluate probabilities without examining all possible outcomes. These two distributions have one essential difference—the method of sampling. In one case the sampling is done *without replacement*, and in the other it is done *with replacement*. Let us introduce these distributions by means of example, and then develop the underlying equations.

hypergeometric distributions

A *hypergeometric distribution* results from sampling without replacement from a population which contains n_1 successes and n_2 failures such that $n_1 + n_2$ equals the entire population. For example, suppose we draw five cards from an unmarked, well-shuffled deck, and we want to know the probability of three of these cards being aces. One method of determining this probability would be to deal millions of hands of cards and count the number of hands that gave the desired results. After a great deal of time, we could take the ratio of those that passed the test to the total number of hands dealt and have an approximation of the probability. To find the actual probability by this means would in fact require dealing an infinite number of hands. Another approach would be to use some of the counting techniques discussed earlier. However, the probability value that we determine by any counting method may never be exactly verified by counting an infinite number of hands. We must *assume* certain characteristics about the deck of cards, and the validity of our calculations is then based on the validity of our assumptions. First, we assume that by shuffling the cards we are actually able to generate a random sample. We further assume that the deck has four suits, and that each suit has 13 cards ranging from ace to king; there are thus four of each card magnitude in the deck, and the deck contains 52 cards.

To simplify our problem we will also assume the order of a deal producing the desired hand of three aces in five cards. Suppose the first card drawn is an ace; we have four chances out of 52 to draw an ace. Suppose the next card drawn is not an ace; we now have 48 chances of drawing a *non*-ace from the remaining 51 cards. That is, the probabilities in this case are

$$P_1 = \tfrac{4}{52} \qquad P_2 = \tfrac{48}{51} \qquad P_3 = \tfrac{3}{50} \qquad P_4 = \tfrac{47}{49} \qquad P_5 = \tfrac{2}{48}$$

where the first, third, and last cards are assumed to be aces.

Expanding on our concept in Eq. 3-5, we see that the probability of this hand, $P(X)$, will be the product of the individual probabilities for each card,

$$P(X) = P_1 P_2 P_3 P_4 P_5 = \tfrac{4}{52} \times \tfrac{48}{51} \times \tfrac{3}{50} \times \tfrac{47}{49} \times \tfrac{2}{48}$$

As already noted, we have specified the order of the deal. We now need to consider the number of ways we can obtain three aces out of five cards. Equation 3-17 provides the answer:

$$C_3^5 = \frac{5!}{3!2!} = 10$$

Since any other deal that gave the same results would merely change the order of the numerators, we can now say that the probability of such a hand is

$$C_3^5 P(X) = 10\left(\frac{4}{52} \times \frac{48}{51} \times \frac{3}{50} \times \frac{47}{49} \times \frac{2}{48}\right) = \frac{94}{54,145}$$

$$= 1.735 \times 10^{-3}$$

The form in which such a hypergeometric distribution is usually stated is

$$P(X) = \frac{C_X^A C_{n-X}^B}{C_n^{A+B}} \qquad\qquad 3\text{-}18$$

where X = number of successes in the sample of size n

A = number of successes in the population from which the sample is taken

B = failures

An example will show that this equation yields the same results as our intuitive approach (the mathematical derivation is beyond our scope). From Eq. 3-18, the probability of the hand is

$$P(X) = \frac{C_3^4 C_2^{48}}{C_5^{52}} = \frac{(4!/3!1!)(48!/46!2!)}{52!/47!5!}$$

$$= \frac{4!}{3!1!} \frac{48!}{46!2!} \frac{47!5!}{52!} = \frac{4!48!5!47!}{3!46!2!52!}$$

$$= \frac{4!(48 \times 47)5!}{3!2!(52 \times 51 \times 50 \times 49 \times 48)}$$

$$= \frac{5!}{3!2!} \frac{4!(48 \times 47)}{52 \times 51 \times 50 \times 49 \times 48}$$

$$= C_3^5 \frac{4 \times 3 \times 2 \times 48 \times 47}{52 \times 51 \times 50 \times 49 \times 48} = \frac{94}{54,145}$$

$$= 1.735 \times 10^{-3}$$

This agrees exactly with our previous solution.

Let us now consider a further example.

example 3-16 An examination is to be given a group of students in a particular course. In order to discourage cheating, the professor writes two separate tests and makes 50 copies of each. He distributes these randomly to his class of 50; what is the probability that exactly half the class has exam 1?

In this case

$$X = 25 \qquad A = 50 \qquad B = 50 \qquad n = 50$$

From Eq. 3-18,

$$P(X) = \frac{C_{25}^{50} C_{25}^{50}}{C_{50}^{100}} = \frac{(50!/25!25!)(50!/25!25!)}{100!/50!50!}$$

$$= \frac{50!50!50!50!}{25!25!25!25!100!}$$

This is not easily evaluated, but a table of factorials can be used to produce an approximate solution:

$100! = 9.3326 \times 10^{157}$ $50! = 3.0414 \times 10^{64}$

$25! = 1.5511 \times 10^{25}$

Hence the probability that half the class has exam 1 is

$$P(X) = \frac{(3.0414 \times 10^{64})^4}{(1.5511 \times 10^{25})^4(9.3326 \times 10^{157})}$$

$$= \frac{3.0414^4 \times 10^{256}}{(1.5511^4 \times 10^{100})(9.3326 \times 10^{157})} = \frac{82 \times 10^{256}}{54.7 \times 10^{257}}$$

$$= \frac{82}{547} = 0.150$$

This example points out one of the main disadvantages of the hypergeometric distribution, the evaluation of the factorial of large numbers. In this regard even high-speed digital computers are limited to the evaluation of factorials of rather small numbers. A table of factorials is given as Appendix F.

binomial distributions

The *binomial distribution* results from sampling with replacement from a population containing n_1 successes and n_2 failures such that $n_1 + n_2$ equals the entire population. To clarify the difference between binomial and hypergeometric distributions let us consider the same basic example of drawing five cards from a deck with the probability that three of these five cards will be aces. This time, however, after each card is selected, it will be replaced in the deck and the entire deck will be reshuffled. Thus we now have the possibility of selecting the same card twice. In this case the probabilities for each card are

$$P_1 = \tfrac{4}{52} \qquad P_2 = \tfrac{48}{52} \qquad P_3 = \tfrac{4}{52} \qquad P_4 = \tfrac{48}{52} \qquad P_5 = \tfrac{4}{52}$$

Now, from Eq. 3-4, the probability of the given hand becomes

$$P(X) = P_1 P_2 P_3 P_4 P_5 = (\tfrac{4}{52})^3 \times (\tfrac{48}{52})^2$$

If we consider the problem of order of cards, the final probability of obtaining three aces in a five-card draw is

$$P(X) = C_3^5 \left(\frac{4}{52}\right)^3 \left(\frac{48}{52}\right)^2 = \frac{5!}{(5-3)!} \left(\frac{4}{52}\right)^3 \left(\frac{48}{52}\right)^2$$

$$= 10 \times 0.077^3 \times 0.923^2 = 3.82 \times 10^{-3}$$

This is easily evaluated by means of a slide rule with log-log scales. The answer supports our intuitive conclusion that we have a better chance of producing the desired hand if we replace the cards as we draw them.

Now let us consider a more general form of the binomial distribution. In this equation the probability of success is presented as P, and X is the number of successes in a sample of n:

$$P(X) = C_x^{\,n} P^x (1 - P)^{n-x} \qquad\qquad \textbf{\textit{3-19}}$$

It is apparent that the values $P = (4/52)$, $n = 5$, and $x = 3$ yield the exact numerical results above.

One further point can now be presented in terms of the data from Example 3-16. Since there are 50 of each type of examinations, the equation takes on a simpler form for evaluation; however, the results would be similar if P were not exactly 0.5. Suppose

$$P = 0.5 \qquad 1 - P = 0.5 \qquad n = 50 \qquad X = 25$$

Then

$$P(X) = C_{25}^{50} \times 0.5^{25} \times 0.5^{25} = \frac{50!}{25!25!} \, 0.5^{50}$$

$$= \frac{3.0414 \times 10^{64}}{(1.5511 \times 10^{25})^2} \times 0.5^{50} = 0.1123$$

Note that this approximates the answer from the hypergeometric distribution shown in Example 3-16; this holds true when n is large. In the next chapter we will deal with the concepts of statistics, which follow directly from the concept of probability.

SUMMARY

An understanding of the underlying concepts of probability are necessary to deal with random or accidental errors. Simple probability P is the ratio of the number of successful outcomes N to the number of total outcomes N_T. However, close attention must be given to the terminology of probability situations. Mutually exclusive events are such that not more than one of them can occur in a single trial. Independent events are such that the outcome of one is not influenced by the occurrence of the other. Conversely, if the occurrence of one event is influenced by the outcome of another, the events are dependent.

In outlining the concepts of probability the Venn diagram, which is a graphic representation of the possible outcomes, provides a useful illustration of the relationships.

Counting techniques are a computational tool for probability evaluations. Permutation is an important technique for determining the number of ways of selecting a group of items where arrangement or order is important. A group of items in which order is not important may be selected by the method of combinations. This leads to two important probability distributions, which differ only in the method of sampling. The hypergeometric distribution results from sampling without replacement a population which contains n_1 successes and n_2 failures such that $n_1 + n_2$ equals the entire population. The binomial distribution results from sampling with replacement a population containing n_1 successes and n_2 failures such that $n_1 + n_2$ equals the entire population.

PROBLEMS

3-1 Calculate the following probabilities for a single roll of one die:
- *a* A two or a three or a four
- *b* A one or a three or a five
- *c* A two or a six
- *d* A five
- *e* A seven
- *f* A five and a six

3-2 Draw a Venn diagram depicting the following conditions (shade the appropriate portion or portions of the diagram):
- *a* Two mutually exclusive events A and B
- *b* Both A and B

c   Neither A nor B
d A but not B
e   Either A or B, but not both
f   Either A or B
g   Event $\overline{A}$

3-3 From a well-shuffled standard 52-card deck and a single draw, what is the probability of obtaining the following cards?
a   A red king
b   A black card
c   A three, a four, a five, or a six
d   A red queen or a black queen

3-4 What is the probability of drawing three aces in succession if the cards are not put back into the deck after they have been drawn?

3-5 In a single roll of three dice, what is the probability of obtaining a four, a five, and a six?

3-6 If P_1 and P_2 are mutually exclusive events, what is the probability that P_1 and P_2 will occur?

3-7 What is the probability of obtaining a three and a four on a single roll of two dice?

3-8 What is the probability of drawing an ace and a king, in that order, from an ordinary deck by drawing two cards in succession? By drawing a single card, replacing it, and taking a second card?

3-9 Using three dice and 216 throws, plot the experimental frequency curve of the sums that occur and then compare this with the theoretical curve.

Total	3	4	5	6	7	8	9	10	11	12	13	14	15	16	17	18
Theoretical frequency	1	3•	6	10	15	21	25	27	27	25	21	15	10	6	3	1

3-10 If a single die is rolled four times, what is the probability of the following rolls?
    a   An ace once
    b   An ace twice
    c   An ace three times
    d   An ace four times
    e   No ace

3-11 Use Venn diagrams to verify the following expressions:
    a $\overline{A + B} = \overline{A}\overline{B}$
    b $\overline{AB} = \overline{A} + \overline{B}$

3-12 Try to verify $A + B + C = A - BC + (C + B)$ with a Venn diagram.

3-13 If A and B are mutually exclusive events, with $P(A) = 0.28$ and $P(B) = 0.46$, what are the following probabilities?
    a $P(A + B)$
    b $P(AB)$
    c $P(B|A)$
    d $P(\overline{A}\overline{B})$ given $\overline{A + B} = \overline{A}\overline{B}$

3-14 If A and B are independent events, with $P(A) = 0.20$ and $P(B) = 0.45$, what are the following probabilities?
    a $P(A + B)$
    b $P(AB)$
    c $P(B|A)$
    d $P(\overline{A}\overline{B})$ given $\overline{A + B} = \overline{A}\overline{B}$

3-15 If one marksman hits the bull's-eye 70 percent of the time and another hits it 60 percent of the time, what is the probability that at least one of them will hit the bull's-eye if both fire at the target simultaneously?

3-16 Suppose the probability that a missile propulsion system will work perfectly is 0.95 and the probability its guidance system will perform without failure is 0.85. What is the probability of a successful flight—that is, that the propulsion system works perfectly and the missile responds to guidance? What is the probability that the propulsion system works or that the missile responds to guidance or both?

3-17 Suppose equal supplies of light bulbs from company *A* and company *B* are intermixed, so that it is not possible to distinguish the two types. If company *A* is known to produce bulbs that are 95 percent reliable and company *B* produces bulbs that are 98 percent reliable, what is the probability of selecting at random a defective bulb from company *A*? Selecting at random a defective bulb from company *B*?

3-18 By mistake, 20 defective transistors became mixed with 15 normal transistors. It is not possible to tell them apart by appearance alone. If two transistors are checked in succession, what are the following probabilities?
    a First a defective transistor and then a normal transistor
    b First a normal transistor and then a defective transistor
    c Either of these two outcomes
    d Two defective transistors
    e Two normal transistors

3-19 If 10 percent of a certain batch of radar components is defective, what is the probability that the first three components you check will be defective and the fourth will be good?

3-20 Suppose eight bulbs wired in series do not light because of one bad bulb. If you change a bulb at random, what is the probability that the string will light?

3-21 An engineer suspects that the products in a process under his control are 3 percent defective. The products are tested by taking random samples of 100 on five consecutive days, with the following results. What do you feel is the percentage of defective products?

Day	Mon.	Tues.	Wed.	Thurs.	Fri.
No. of defective products	4	3	4	2	2

3-22 An engineer has data indicating that the chances that a given bridge will fail under the loads he expects are one in a thousand. A better bridge would cost $10,000 more. If losses for bridge failure are $7 million for lawsuits and other costs, should the better bridge be built?

3-23 As an engineer in charge of maintaining certain equipment, you are faced with the problem of ordering and stockpiling certain spare parts. The limitations on the number of spares are cost, storage space, and possible replacement of equipment. Suggest a method of ordering spares.

3-24 If contestants are required to predict the outcomes (win, lose, tie) of 20 different football games, what is the total number of possible outcomes? Assuming no prior knowledge of the team's records, what is the probability of picking 20 games correctly?

3-25 In how many ways may a club of 30 members elect a president and a vice-president?

3-26 If a certain tire manufacturer wants to test five different tread designs at four different speeds on four different types of road surfaces, how many different tests must he make?

3-27 In dog racing one of the rarest occurrences is that the eight greyhounds will finish in perfect numerical order. What are the odds against such a finish?

3-28 Evaluate the following numbers:

a $10!$

b $\dfrac{9!}{5!}$

c $\dfrac{17!}{0!}$

d $\dfrac{43!}{21!}$

e $\dfrac{14!12!}{9!}$

3-29   Evaluate the following:

   a C_7^{10}
   b C_9^{15}
   c P_8^{20}
   d P_{13}^{47}

3-30   How many lineups are possible in making up a five-man basketball team to be selected at random from 10 players?

3-31   Compute the number of possible five-card hands from a standard 52-card deck.

3-32   Show that $C_r{}^n = C_{n-r}^n$.

3-33   How many ways can 10 objects be selected from a group of 20 when order is important? When order is not important?

3-34   The major of a town is asked to appoint a technical committee consisting of four engineers and three architects. The local engineering society submitted a list of 12 engineers and the architect organization a list of 10 architects from which to make the appointments. How many possible committees are there?

3-35   If a technical committee of four members is to be selected from nine engineers and five physicists, how many possible committees are there? In how many ways may the committee be chosen if it is to have just three engineers?

3-36   If you flip a fair coin 10 times, what is the probability that it will land heads up exactly three times? At least three times?

3-37   Four chests contain five coins each, one of which is a rare coin. Of the four rare coins, one is worth $50,000. By selecting one coin from each chest, what is the probability of selecting two rare coins? Selecting only the $50,000 rare coin?

3-38   In order to find the probability of failure in flashbulbs a sample was taken from a batch of 50. If 10 percent are actually defective, what is the probability of finding one bad bulb in a sample of 10?

3-39 The course supervisor of an engineering class prepared 14 problems for the final examination. If instructors are to select any five problems from this group, how many different combinations are possible? Assume that each problem has an equal chance of being selected.

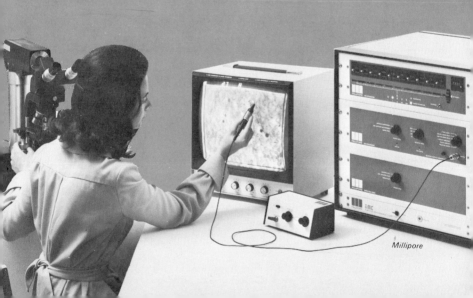

four

basic statistical concepts

In Chapter Three we introduced some of the concepts of probability and the distributions that are governed by the laws of probability. A knowledge of the manner in which a set of values is distributed is very important in many fields, including engineering. To determine whether the probabilities are really equal for any one of the six faces on a fair die would require a great many rolls, or samples, before our actual sample probabilities approached the predicted value; in fact, the number of rolls would have to be infinite for the two values to be equal. Thus we need some way of taking a sample from a set of data and inferring from this sample how the total data are distributed. In this case we may know nothing about the actual distribution of the data except what we learn from our sample; thus the procedure differs from sampling from known probability distributions.

We have delayed until this point a discussion of the general concept of distributions. There are two basic types of distribution, discrete and continuous. A *discrete distribution* is one made up of elementary events that can have only distinct values. For example, if we roll two dice, the digits that turn up can sum to any integer from 2 to 12 and no others. It is not possible for them to sum, say, to 4.5.

In a *continuous distribution* the events may have any value between the given limits. For example, the ball bearings produced by a certain machine may be of any diameter between the maximum and minimum limits. You may recall from earlier studies of mathematics that there are an infinite number of points on a given line segment; in effect, that is what we have in this case. The line segment is made up of all possible values between the two limits and is normally the abscissa of a plot of the distribution.

In this chapter we will consider sampling from a given distribution and attempt to quantify the distribution by mathematical measures. The answers we obtain are usually more reasonable for the continuous distribution, since the events can take on any value. If you were told that the average diameter of ball bearings was 0.51 in., you would assume that this was reasonable; however, a roll of a pair of dice yielding an average of 7.52 has little meaning in relation to any actual outcome possible in such a roll.

Although in Chapter Three we dealt with discrete types of distributions, most of the observations made by engineers are from continuous distributions. We will discuss here only one of many continuous distributions used by engineers—the *normal distribution*, which is explained in Chapter Five. For a complete study of distributions see the advanced texts listed in the References at the end of the book.

4-2 SAMPLING

Before we look at the process of sampling, let us define some of the terms we will be using. A *population* is the total of the data from which a sample is taken. If we were to sample a boxcar of apples to determine the percentage of rotten apples, the population would include every apple in the boxcar. There are some cases, of course, in which the population is infinite. When we refer to a *sample*, we mean not just a portion of the population, but a portion selected such that the observed values have no *bias*. We call this process *random sampling*. For example, if we wanted to determine the percentage of broken bricks in a whole pile of bricks, taking the sample bricks only from the top of the pile would bias the results. In a random sample every member of the population has an equal probability of being selected by pure chance. Suppose we want to select one name at random from a list of 10. We might write all 10 names on a list, pin the list to a wall, and have someone throw a dart at the list. However, the person would actually be "aiming" his throw toward the center of the list; hence the chances of selection would not be equal for all the names. Of course, we might blindfold him, turn him around several times, and then have him throw his dart at the wall the list is on. Then, if he did hit a name, we could be fairly certain that the choice was random and without bias.

In any field in which statistical inferences are drawn from samples there is the problem of determining whether some bias exists that may invalidate the conclusions. In engineering, samples may be obtained by means of specially designed processes and equipment or from *random-number tables*, a collection of numbers selected by chance. The specific techniques of random sampling are discussed in the advanced works on statistics listed in the References. We will assume here that any sample we discuss was randomly selected. We will observe certain characteristics of the sample, and from these we will make inferences about characteristics of the population.

To illustrate some of the basic concepts let us examine sampling first from a graphical standpoint and then comment on sampling techniques and methods of determining sample sizes as we continue with the discussion of statistics.

4-3 HISTOGRAMS

A *histogram* is a graphic display of sample data in which the abscissa indicates the recorded values and the ordinate indicates the frequency of occurrence. Histograms are often used to display statistical data. Consider the histograms in Figs. 4-1 and 4-2, which display the data in Tables 4-1 and 4-2.

grouping

Note that the data in Table 4-1 and Fig. 4-1 give no indication of the exact life of the bulb that failed in the second interval (100 to 199.9 hr). This could be a result of the sampling method; the 400 bulbs could all have been turned on at one time and then checked at the end of each time period for bulbs that had failed during that time. Or the exact number of hours each bulb lasted could have been recorded and then arranged in groups to reduce the total number of observed data points. This technique of grouping is used to smooth out the data for a clearer picture of the underlying distribution. Note that Fig. 4-1 does indeed show the distribution of the data.

Most frequently 10 to 20 groups are desired for this type of display. To determine the cutoff points for each groups we must

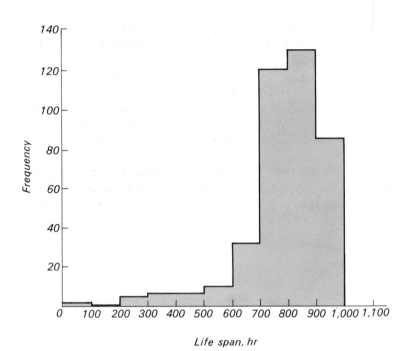

figure 4-1   Life span of 400 light bulbs

table 4-1   Life span of light bulbs (400 bulbs tested)

No. of hours	No. of bulbs failing in this time span
0– 99.9	2
100– 199.9	1
200– 299.9	5
300– 399.9	7
400– 499.9	7
500– 599.9	10
600– 699.9	32
700– 799.9	120
800– 899.9	130
900– 999.9	86
1,000–1099.9	0

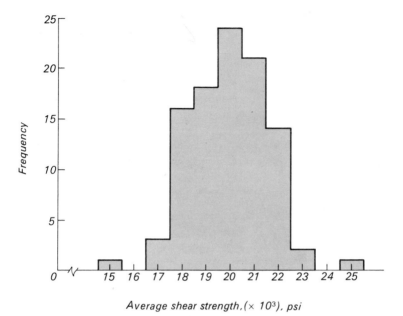

figure 4-2 Average shear strength for 100 steel samples

table 4-2 Average shear strength for 100 steel specimens

Shear stress $\times 10^3$, psi	No. of samples
15	1
16	0
17	3
18	16
19	18
20	24
21	21
22	14
23	2
24	0
25	1

first determine the range of the data. The *range $R(X)$* is the numerical difference between the largest and smallest observed value; that is,

$$R(X) = X_{max} - X_{min} \qquad\qquad \textbf{4-1}$$

A group, or *class interval*, is then selected such that when it is divided into the range the result will be 10 to 20 classes. Let us clarify this point before we discuss more formal methods.

> **example 4-1**   An industrial engineer sampled a work crew to determine performance time for a specific task. He found that the times to perform the task ranged from 15 to 100 sec. How would he group the data into approximately 10 groups for display purposes?
>
> From Eq. 4-1, the range is
>
> $$R(X) = 100 - 15 = 85 \text{ sec}$$
>
> If we assume a class interval of 7 sec, then
>
> $$\frac{85}{7} = 12.2, \text{ or 13 classes}$$
>
> (as only whole classes can be used).

> **example 4-2**   A mechanical engineer is measuring diameters of ball bearings produced by a new machine and finds values ranging from 0.521 to 0.482 in. Select a class interval that will provide approximately 10 to 20 intervals.
>
> The range is
>
> $$R(X) = 0.521 - 0.482 = 0.039$$
>
> Assume a class interval of 0.003 in. Then
>
> $$\frac{0.039}{0.003} = 13 \text{ classes}$$

class boundaries

Our next concern is defining the class boundaries so that we can readily determine into which of two classes a particular observation falls. The boundaries must be such that no observation can have a value that coincides with a boundary. This is normally governed by careful selection of the class-interval value. Note that the value selected for the class interval should always have an odd digit in the least significant place (as in both the preceding examples). Consider Fig. 4-3, which is a graphical sketch of class boundaries for the data in Example 4-2. Note that the class boundaries contain one more significant digit than the observations. Since this digit is always a midpoint between possible observations, there is no difficulty in grouping the data into the chosen classes.

relative frequency

In order to remove the bias of sample size many histograms are plotted with a relative frequency instead of the observed frequency as the ordinate. The *relative frequency* is merely the observed frequency divided by the sample size. This does not alter the shape of the histogram; it only changes the scale of the ordinate. For example, suppose we retake a sample like the one shown in Fig. 4-2, except that this time we observe 200 specimens instead of 100. By using relative frequencies we could plot one set of data over the other to see if they show the same distribution of shear strengths, that is, to see if they belong to the same population.

The histogram enables us to see the actual distribution of the

figure 4-3   Class intervals, midpoints, and boundaries

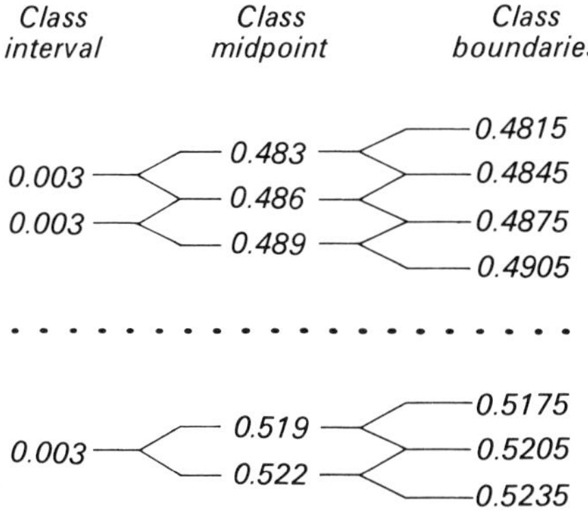

Class interval	Class midpoint	Class boundaries
		0.4815
0.003	0.483	0.4845
0.003	0.486	0.4875
	0.489	0.4905
		0.5175
0.003	0.519	0.5205
	0.522	0.5235

sample data and hence provides a far clearer picture than many of the numerical techniques. If our sample is, as we hope, descriptive of the population, we are now able to describe certain properties of the population. Let us now consider how well the sample does describe the population.

4-4   CENTRAL TENDENCY

One numerical measure used to describe our data is the *central tendency* or *average value.* There are several methods used to measure this concept of "average." The most common is the arithmetic average or *mean.* Two others commonly used when the data are not symmetrical are the *median* and the *mode.* When we are working with samples taken from a population, it is important to realize that the central measure we employ relates only indirectly to the population. This will be discussed in greater detail later.

the mean

If two people were independently to measure one side of an empty lot to the nearest inch with a 12-in. scale, the probability that their results would agree exactly is very low. Which value would be correct? Provided both measurements were taken with equal care, we might reasonably conclude that we should add the two values and divide by 2. This average value would then be our best guess at the length of the lot. We might send out additional measurers, each using the same process and care; if so, we would have to consider each additional observation in determining the apparent length of the field. We might decide once again to sum the observed values and divide by the number of observations to find the *mean.* This relation is expressed as

$$\bar{X} = \sum_{i=1}^{n} \frac{X_i}{n} = \frac{X_1 + X_2 + \cdots + X_n}{n} \qquad \textbf{4-2}$$

where $\bar{X}$ represents the arithmetic mean of a set of observations and X_i refers to the recorded value of the ith observation.

The mean is a primary measure of central tendency which we have been using since our early training in mathematics. It gives equal weight to each observation and may be considered the "balance point" of the sample data. Let us return to the histogram to illustrate this concept. Consider that the abscissa is a measure of distance between groups of observations and that the frequency is the weight of observation. As an example, we might calculate the balance point of a beam (the abscissa) with the various weights (frequencies) shown on the histogram. This balance point would be $\bar{X}$, as defined in Eq. 4-2. This leads to the following interesting observation that the summation of the observed values minus the mean is zero:

$$\sum_{i=1}^{n} (X_i - \bar{X}) = 0 \qquad\qquad 4\text{-}3$$

As proof,

$$\sum_{i=1}^{n} X_i - \sum_{i=1}^{n} \bar{X} = \sum_{i=1}^{n} X_i - n\bar{X}$$

$$= \frac{n}{n} \sum_{i=1}^{n} X_i - n\bar{X} = n\bar{X} - n\bar{X} = 0$$

For a review of the summation notation used here see Appendix D.

the median

If we were given the data in Table 4-1, it would be somewhat unrealistic to evaluate the average life by Eq. 4-2; the bulbs that failed early would influence the resulting value to an unfair degree, and our result would be somewhat lower than what we would consider average. In this situation we would employ a *median*; that is, we would arrange the observations in numerical order from the highest to the lowest, or vice versa, and then select the midpoint of the arranged data as our average. The technique of selecting this midpoint varies, depending on whether the sample size is odd or even. If it is odd, we merely select the midpoint; if it is even, we have to average the middle two values. If we denote the median as $\tilde{X}$, then for an odd number of observations n

$$\tilde{X} = X_k \qquad\qquad \textbf{4-4}$$

where $k = (n + 1)/2$, with data ordered numerically, and for an even number of observations n,

$$\tilde{X} = \frac{X_k + X_{k+1}}{2} \qquad\qquad \textbf{4-5}$$

where $k = n/2$, with data ordered numerically.

One common example of this measure of central tendency is the "average national income." This figure is actually a median income value, used to remove the bias introduced in the arithmetic mean by the extremely high incomes of a very few individuals. Another example is fatigue failure, where a histogram of the data would be similar to Fig. 4-1. In general, we can say that if a histogram shows the distribution to be *skewed* (that is, not symmetrical), then the median is a better average than the mean.

the mode

A second method of describing an average when the data are skewed is the mode. The *mode* is the most frequently occurring value (the highest ordinate of a histogram). For the data in Table 4-1 the mode would be 850, the middle of the 800 to 899.9 interval. This method has certain failings when sample sizes are small, as there may be several observations with the same frequency or there may be very little difference between observed values. Such cases in which there are two or more modes, are referred to as *bimodal* or *multimodal* distributions.

In general, the mean, the median, and the mode will be very close when the data are almost symmetrical and will vary to the extent that the data are skewed right or left. In each case the choice of the method to measure the average depends on the data and their distribution.

4-5 RELATION OF CENTRAL TENDENCY TO POPULATION AND SAMPLES

From this point on we will make the assumption that the populations we are describing are normally distributed. This concept will be expanded in Chapter Five, but for the time being any distribution with the graphical shape of Fig. 4-4 will be considered a normal distribution.

This is not too restrictive an assumption, as the distribution of most observations in engineering work is normal or very close to normal. A simple check is obtained by plotting a histogram to observe the underlying distribution. Since the histogram is produced from a sample of the population, its shape implies some of the characteristics of the population. (For a discussion of other graphical methods of testing data, such as probability plots on special paper, see the References at the end of the book.)

Let us now demonstrate graphically what happens during the sampling process. First we need to establish a consistent notation in order to describe the process. The following notation will be used throughout the remainder of the text.

$\overline{X}_0$ = mean of the population (any subscript 0 refers to the population)

$\overline{X}$ = sample mean

X_i = the ith observed value

E_i = the ith error, $X_i - \overline{X}_0$

$\overline{E}$ = average or mean error

n = size of sample

N = size of population

figure *4-4   A normal distribution*

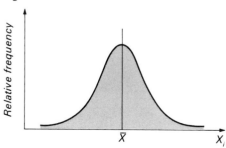

We will assume that we are able to observe the entire population of size N, that is, that the population is finite. We will also assume that we can select several samples of size n from the population, with $n < N$. We calculate both $\bar{X}_0$ and $\bar{X}$ for all sets of observation. Some possible results are shown in Fig. 4-5. The darker curve represents the actual distribution of the entire population, and $\bar{X}_0$ is its mean. Two other samples selected randomly are shown as the lighter curves; one has a mean $\bar{X}_1$ which is less than that for the population, and the other has a mean $\bar{X}_2$ which is greater than that for the population. If we had written all the X_i for the population on slips of paper and placed them in a box, samples 1 and 2 could have been selected by taking a slip of paper from the box, recording it, and then replacing it and stirring all the slips before making the next selection. Thus it is pure chance that the observations for sample 1 include many of the lowest values of X_i from the population and sample 2 contains predominately higher values of X_i. The point is that during a random sample, when the whole population is not observed, the sample data will tend to yield $\bar{X}$ slightly different from $\bar{X}_0$. Of course, the difference between $\bar{X}_0$ and the sample $\bar{X}$ is greatly exaggerated in Fig. 4-5 for the sake of illustration. Our problem now is to analyze this difference between the actual mean $\bar{X}_0$ and sample mean $\bar{X}$.

We have defined the error E_i as the difference between an observation X_i and the true mean $\bar{X}_0$; the total relationship of

figure *4-5   Difference between population and sample means*

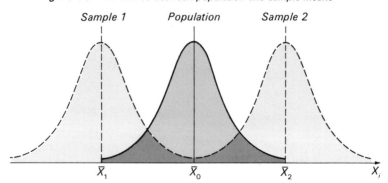

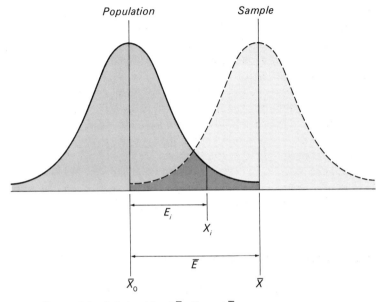

figure 4-6 *Relationship of $\overline{X}_0$, X_i, and $\overline{X}$*

$\overline{X}_0$, X_i, E_i, and $\overline{E}$ is shown in Fig. 4-6. Only the case $\overline{X} > \overline{X}_0$ is shown, but this can be extended to the case $\overline{X} < \overline{X}_0$. Some of the relationships shown in Fig. 4-6 are derived as follows:

$$\overline{X} = \sum_{i=1}^{n} \frac{X_i}{n} \qquad X_i = \overline{X}_0 + E_i$$

$$\overline{X} = \sum_{i=1}^{n} \frac{\overline{X}_0 + E_i}{n} = \frac{n\overline{X}_0}{n} + \sum_{i=1}^{n} \frac{E_i}{n} = \overline{X}_0 + \overline{E}$$

Note that since we have defined $E_i = X_i - \overline{X}_0$, we have

$$\sum_{i=1}^{N} \frac{E_i}{N} = 0$$

where N is the size of the population (see Fig. 4-3).

We can see that $\sum_{i=1}^{n} (E_i/n)$ gets smaller as n gets larger. This is because E_i can be positive or negative, and when $n = N$ the summation is zero. This difference between $\bar{X}_0$ and $\bar{X}$ is a function of the size of our sample, and ideally we can make the difference as small as we wish by increasing the sample size until it approaches that of the population.

In this section we have assumed that we were able to measure the entire population, a situation that is in fact rarely possible. The statements based on this assumption are valid, but we must now extend them to the real world. Since we are unable to measure $\bar{X}_0$, and hence unable to evaluate E_i, we are never sure of the extent of the mean error $\bar{E}$ between the sample $\bar{X}$ and $\bar{X}_0$. We do know that we can reduce this error by increasing the sample size. Sample-size considerations will be discussed in Chapter Five.

4-6   ACTUAL EVALUATION OF THE SAMPLE MEAN

In Section 4-4 we defined the sample mean as $\bar{X} = \Sigma X_i/n$. There are several ways to evaluate this term. We rarely calculate $\bar{X}$ by Eq. 4-2, since without the aid of a calculator or computer the chance for error with extensive data is quite high. There are, however, methods that allow us to evaluate $\bar{X}$ rapidly and quite accurately by hand. These methods usually entail working with grouped data, as given in Tables 4-1 and 4-2, and thus require a slight modification of our basic equation 4-2. If we let f_j denote the frequency in the jth group of m groups, then

$$n = \sum_{j=1}^{m} f_j \quad \text{and} \quad \sum_{i=1}^{n} X_i = \sum_{j=1}^{m} f_j X_j$$

where X_j is the group value of X. Therefore we may write the sample mean as

$$\bar{X} = \frac{\displaystyle\sum_{j=1}^{m} f_j X_j}{\displaystyle\sum_{j=1}^{m} f_j} \qquad \textbf{4-6}$$

We can use Eq. 4-6 to put the data from Table 4-2 in the form shown in Table 4-3. Then

$$\Sigma f_j = 100 \qquad \Sigma f_j X_j = 1{,}996$$

and substitution in Eq. 4-6 yields

$$\overline{X} = \frac{\sum_{j=1}^{11} f_j X_j}{\sum_{j=1}^{11} f_j} = \frac{1{,}996}{100} = 19.96$$

and

$$\overline{X} = 19.96 \times 10^3 \text{ psi}$$

We note right away that some of the individual terms $f_j X_j$ are not easy to multiply, and the multiplication would be even more difficult if the X_j terms included decimal portions. Let us therefore introduce an additional modification to the calculation—one where we start with an assumed mean $\overline{X}'$. We let $v_j' = X_j - \overline{X}'$, so that we now use v_j' in our calculation of $\overline{X}$. Here v_j' is the difference between an observation X_j and the apparent mean $\overline{X}'$ and is sometimes referred to as the *apparent variation.*

table 4-3 *Evaluation of average shear strength ($\times 10^3$) for 100 steel specimens*

j	f_j	X_j	$f_j X_j$
1	1	15	15
2	0	16	0
3	3	17	51
4	16	18	288
5	18	19	342
6	24	20	480
7	21	21	441
8	14	22	308
9	2	23	46
10	0	24	0
11	1	25	25
	100		1996

With this notation we may write

$$v'_j = X_j - \overline{X}' \qquad X_j = v'_j + \overline{X}'$$

$$\overline{X} = \frac{\sum\limits_{j=1}^{m} f_j X_j}{n} = \frac{\sum\limits_{j=1}^{m} f_j(v'_j + \overline{X}')}{n}$$

Expanding the numerator (it is customary to omit the limits on the summations for ease of reading), we have

$$\Sigma f_j(v'_j + \overline{X}') = \Sigma f_j v'_j + \Sigma f_j \overline{X}' = \Sigma f_j v'_j + n\overline{X}'$$

since $\Sigma f_j = n$. Thus

$$\overline{X} = \frac{\sum\limits_{j=1}^{m} f_j v'_j}{n} + \overline{X}' \qquad\qquad\qquad 4\text{-}7$$

Table 4-4 shows this modification applied to the data in Table 4-2. Thus if

$$\overline{X}' = 20.00$$

we see that

$$\Sigma f_j v'_j = -4$$

table 4-4 Evaluation of average shear strength
($\times 10^3$) with an assumed mean

j	X_j	v'_j	f_j	$f_j v'_j$
1	15	−5	1	−5
2	16	−4	0	0
3	17	−3	3	−9
4	18	−2	16	−32
5	19	−1	18	−18
6	20	0	24	0
7	21	1	21	21
8	22	2	14	28
9	23	3	2	6
10	24	4	0	0
11	25	5	1	5
			100	−4

and

$$\bar{X} = \frac{\Sigma f_j v'_j}{n} + \bar{X}' = \frac{-4}{100} + 20.00$$

or

$$\bar{X} = 19.96 \times 10^3 \text{ psi}$$

This method tends to eliminate errors, but several precautions are needed. First, it is usually a good idea to have the X_j values in order, either ascending or descending, and care must be taken to see that v'_j is actually calculated from its defining equation.

There is one final improvement for grouped data when the class interval is not equal to 1. For this case we redefine the difference v'_j as

$$v'_j = \frac{X_j - \bar{X}'}{I}$$

where I is the class interval. We now restate the equation for $\bar{X}$ as

$$I v'_j = X_j - \bar{X}' \qquad \bar{X} = \frac{\Sigma f_j X_j}{n}$$

$$\bar{X} = \frac{\Sigma f_j (I v'_j + \bar{X}')}{n}$$

Expanding the numerator yields

$$\bar{X} = I \frac{\sum_{j=1}^{m} f_j v'_j}{n} + \bar{X}' \qquad\qquad \textbf{4-8}$$

Note that Eq. 4-7 is a special case of Eq. 4-8 when $I = 1$. To show the use of this equation, consider Table 4-5, which shows data for the moisture content of 20 soil samples from a highway embankment.

The class interval is $I = 0.3$ and the assumed mean is $\bar{X}' = 16.4$. From Table 4-5, we see that

$$\Sigma f_j = 20 \qquad \Sigma f_j v'_j = 14$$

Then, from Eq. 4-8,

table 4-5 *Evaluation of average moisture content (percent) of 20 samples with assumed mean and class interval*

j	Boundaries	X_j	Iv_j	v'_j	f_j	$f_j v'_j$
	14.45					
1		14.6	−1.8	−6	1	−6
	14.75					
2		14.9	−1.5	−5	1	−5
	15.05					
3		15.2	−1.2	−4	1	−4
	15.35					
4		15.5	−0.9	−3	1	−3
	15.65					
5		15.8	−0.6	−2	3	−6
	15.95					
6		16.1	−0.3	−1	1	−1
	16.25					
7		16.4	0	0	1	0
	16.55					
8		16.7	0.3	1	2	2
	16.85					
9		17.0	0.6	2	2	4
	17.15					
10		17.3	0.9	3	2	6
	17.45					
11		17.6	1.2	4	1	4
	17.75					
12		17.9	1.5	5	1	5
	18.05					
13		18.2	1.8	6	3	18
					20	14

$$\overline{X} = \frac{I \sum_{j=1}^{m} f_j v'_j}{n} + \overline{X}' = \frac{0.3 \times 14}{20} + 16.4$$

$$= 16.61, \text{ or } 16.6 \text{ percent moisture content}$$

We are now able to calculate any $\overline{X}$ regardless of the nature of the data by summing the frequency of observations times some integer. Whether the actual form we use is Eq. 4-2, 4-6, 4-7, or 4-8 will depend on the amount of data and the availability of calculators or computers to assist in the evaluation. We will return to the mean later when we expand on the basic concepts of statistics.

4-7 *DISPERSION OF DATA: VARIANCE AND STANDARD DEVIATION*

A second desired measure of the data is a description of its *dispersion*, or the extent of its scatter. Several methods have been developed to place a value on the amount of dispersion so that sets of data might be compared. We have discussed the concept of range. Another such description is the *standard deviation*, which is the accepted statistical measure of dispersion. All the distributions in Fig. 4-7 have exactly the same range, but it is obvious that the data are not dispersed in the same way. Therefore we need some measure of the dispersion that indicates such differences in the distribution of data.

It has been found in analyzing data that a good measure of dispersion is the *variance*, the summation of the squared difference between each observation and the mean $\bar{X}_0$, divided by the sample size. If we denote the variance as $\sigma_0{}^2$, we may write this relation as

figure *4-7 · Dispersion in several distributions*

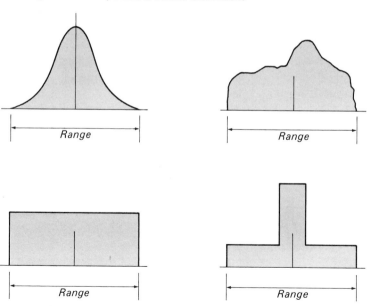

$$\sigma_0{}^2 = \frac{\sum_{i=1}^{n}(X_i - \bar{X}_0)^2}{n} = \frac{\Sigma(X_i{}^2 - 2X_i\bar{X}_0 + \bar{X}_0{}^2)}{n}$$

$$= \frac{\Sigma X_i{}^2 - 2\Sigma X_i\bar{X}_0 + \Sigma\bar{X}_0{}^2}{n}$$

$$= \frac{\Sigma X_i{}^2 - 2n/n\,\Sigma X_i\bar{X}_0 + n\bar{X}_0{}^2}{n}$$

$$n\sigma_0{}^2 = \Sigma X_i{}^2 - 2n\bar{X}_0{}^2 + n\bar{X}_0{}^2 = \Sigma X_i{}^2 - n\bar{X}_0{}^2$$

Thus we may express the variance as

$$\sigma_0{}^2 = \frac{\Sigma X_i{}^2}{n} - \bar{X}_0{}^2 \qquad\qquad \textbf{4-9}$$

Recall that we are rarely able to evaluate $\bar{X}_0$. We can define an approximation for $\sigma_0{}^2$ in terms of our sample data and $\bar{X}$. However, in using the sample to evaluate the sample mean $\bar{X}$ and then using $\bar{X}$ as the estimate of the population mean $\bar{X}_0$ in the expansion for the variance, we are introducing an error. Our sum of the squares with $\bar{X}$ will be smaller than if it had been taken about $\bar{X}_0$. To correct this we must divide the entire sum by $n - 1$, instead of n, as in the definition of σ_0. Thus

$$\sigma_0{}^2 \simeq \sigma_s{}^2 = \frac{\sum_{i=1}^{n}(X_i - \bar{X})^2}{n - 1} \qquad\qquad \textbf{4-10}$$

where $\sigma_s{}^2$ is the approximated variance. This adjustment, often referred to as the *Bessel correction*, is discussed in more advanced texts on statistics. It yields satisfactory results for sample sizes greater than 25, but for sample sizes smaller than 25 the results are questionable.

Note that the units of $\sigma_0{}^2$ or $\sigma_s{}^2$ are not those we observed but are instead the square of the observed units. We define the *standard deviation* σ_0 or σ_s, in terms of the observed units. Thus

$$\sigma_0 = \sqrt{\frac{\sum_{i=1}^{n} (X_i - \overline{X}_0)^2}{n}} \qquad \sigma_s = \sqrt{\frac{\sum_{i=1}^{n} (X_i - \overline{X})^2}{n-1}} \qquad \textbf{\textit{4-11}}$$

Although the standard deviation provides us with a measure of dispersion even for data that are not normally distributed, it has an added advantage for normally distributed data. As we will see in Chapter Five, it is one of the defining parameters for the normal distribution.

4-8 ACTUAL EVALUATION OF THE STANDARD DEVIATION

As in evaluating the mean, we often find it convenient to use equations slightly different from the defining equations to evaluate the standard deviation. Let us illustrate with a series of equations paralleling those in Sec. 4-6. Using the convention of Eq. 4-6, we can rewrite Eq. 4-10 directly as

$$\sigma_s^2 = \frac{\sum_{j=1}^{m} f_j (X_j - \overline{X})^2}{n-1}$$

Since the numbers obtained from this form of the equation are awkward to work with, we will proceed to an extension of the convention used in Eq. 4-7. This procedure is known as *coding*, or the short method. We write

$$X_j = v_j' + \overline{X}' \qquad \text{and} \qquad \sigma_s^2 = \frac{\sum_{j=1}^{m} f_j (v_j' + \overline{X}' - \overline{X})^2}{n-1}$$

to obtain

$$(n-1)\sigma_s^2 = \sum_{j=1}^{m} f_j \left[(v_j' + \overline{X}') - \left(\overline{X}' + \frac{\sum_{j=1}^{m} f_j v_j'}{n} \right) \right]^2$$

$$= \sum_{j=1}^{m} f_j \left[v_j' - \frac{\sum_{j=1}^{m} f_j v_j'}{n} \right]^2$$

$$= \Sigma f_j \left[v_j'^2 - 2v_j' \frac{\Sigma f_j v_j'}{n} + \left(\frac{\Sigma f_j v_j'}{n} \right)^2 \right]$$

where all summations are from $j = 1$ to $j = m$. Then, multiplying the second term by n/n, we have

$$(n - 1)\sigma_s^2 = \Sigma f_j v_j'^2 - 2n \frac{\Sigma f_j v_j'}{n} \frac{\Sigma f_j v_j'}{n} + n \left(\frac{\Sigma f_j v_j'}{n} \right)^2$$

$$= \Sigma f_j v_j'^2 - 2n \left(\frac{\Sigma f_j v_j'}{n} \right)^2 + n \left(\frac{\Sigma f_j v_j'}{n} \right)^2$$

$$= \Sigma f_j v_j'^2 - n \left(\frac{\Sigma f_j v_j'}{n} \right)^2$$

Therefore

$$\sigma_s = \sqrt{ \frac{\Sigma f_j v_j'^2 - n \left(\dfrac{\Sigma f_j v_j'}{n} \right)^2}{n - 1} }$$

or

$$\sigma_s = \sqrt{\frac{n}{n - 1}} \sqrt{ \frac{\Sigma f_j v_j'^2}{n} - \left(\frac{\Sigma f_j v_j'}{n} \right)^2 } \qquad \textbf{4-12}$$

An example of the use of Eq. 4-12 is in order. Using the same data that were applied to Eq. 4-7, we establish Table 4-6, from which we obtain

$$\Sigma f_j = n = 100 \qquad \Sigma f_j v_j' = -4 \qquad \Sigma f_j v_j'^2 = 254$$

Then, from Eq. 4-12,

$$\sigma_s = \sqrt{\frac{n}{n-1}} \sqrt{\frac{\Sigma f_j v_j'^2}{n} - \left(\frac{\Sigma f_j v_j'}{n}\right)^2}$$

$$= \pm \sqrt{\frac{100}{99}} \sqrt{\frac{254}{100} - \left(\frac{-4}{100}\right)^2} = 1.005 \times (2.54 - 0.0016)^{\frac{1}{2}}$$

$$= 1.60$$

or

$$\sigma_s = \pm 1.60 \times 10^3 \text{ psi}$$

If we extend the general form of Eq. 4-8 by the same technique, we obtain

$$\sigma_s = I\sqrt{\frac{n}{n-1}} \sqrt{\frac{\Sigma f_j v_j'^2}{n} - \left(\frac{\Sigma f_j v_j'}{n}\right)^2} \qquad \textbf{4-13}$$

The use of this equation is straightforward and follows the previous example, except that the result is multiplied by the class interval I. We will see in the following chapters that we can use $\overline{X}$ and σ_s evaluated from samples to approximate $\overline{X}_0$ and σ_0 for a population, provided the samples are large enough. Since $\overline{X}$ approaches $\overline{X}_0$ as the sample size get larger, the general equation for σ_s varies from that for σ_0 by the denominator, which becomes

table 4-6 *Extension of Table 4-4 to evaluate standard deviation of shear strength (× 10³ psi)*

j	f_j	v_j'	$f_j v_j'$	$f_j v_j'^2$
1	1	−5	−5	25
2	0	−4	0	0
3	3	−3	−9	27
4	16	−2	−32	64
5	18	−1	−18	18
6	24	0	0	0
7	21	1	21	21
8	14	2	28	56
9	2	3	6	18
10	0	4	0	0
11	1	5	5	25
	100		−4	254

insignificant as n gets large. But how large a sample is "large enough"? That is, how large should n be for our assumptions of $\bar{X}$ and σ_s to be valid? The general consensus of statisticians is that if the sample is smaller than 25 or 30, we are statistically on thin ice; with a sample of this size or larger, our inferences about the population are likely to be valid.

SUMMARY

A set of data may be sampled to provide statistical information about its underlying characteristics. The population is the total data from which a sample is taken. A sample is an observed portion of the population, which we have assumed to be a random sample.

The sample data are often represented by a histogram, a graphical plot of the frequency versus the values that provides a clear picture of the distribution. An important part of making a histogram is grouping of the observations and the selection of proper boundaries for these groups.

One of the most important descriptions of the distribution of data is its central tendency. A common measure of central tendency is the arithmetic mean $\bar{X}$, evaluated by summing the values of all the observations and dividing by the total number of observations. Two less important measures of central tendency are the median $\tilde{X}$, which is the central value of the ordered data, and the mode, which is the most frequently occurring value.

For a complete description of the data a measure of dispersion is required. The most widely accepted measure of dispersion is the variance σ_0^2, generally expressed as the standard deviation σ_0.

In order to draw statistical inferences from a sample, the sample must be large enough not to influence the statistical validity of our results.

PROBLEMS

4-1   Use the defining equations to calculate the mean and standard deviation for the following measurements, in inches:

   1.8   2.0   1.8   1.9   2.0

4-2 Plot a histogram for each of the following sets of numbers and determine if they represent a normal distribution:

a   1   2   3   4   5
    6   7   8   9   10
   11   12   13   14   15
   16   17   18   19   20

b 5.39   5.39   5.38   5.37   5.40   5.41
   5.39   5.40   5.42   5.41   5.38   5.37
   5.39   5.39   5.36   5.40   5.40   5.39
   5.38   5.39   5.38   5.39   5.40   5.38

c 215   200   220   230   210
   225   230   205   225   220
   225   215   220   225   230
   220   225   225   220   230

d 0.740   0.736   0.735   0.741   0.735
   0.737   0.738   0.739   0.736   0.737
   0.738   0.737   0.736   0.735   0.736
   0.735   0.735   0.736   0.737   0.736

4-3 For the following data on the resistance of resistors make a frequency graph and estimate the mean and the range:

Number	Resistance, ohms
2	50–52
5	52–54
15	54–56
25	56–58
49	58–60
52	60–62
27	62–64
16	64–66
4	66–68
2	68–70

4-4 Find the arithmetic mean, median, and mode for the following sets of numbers:

a   4   5   6   3   7   *b*   6   7   8   9   7
   8   9   10   7   6   6   5   6   7   8
   5   4   6   7   6   6   5

4-5 For the set of numbers

7.5   6.8   8.3   7.0   6.9
6.8   7.1   6.8   6.9   7.0

Find the mean to three significant figures, the median, the mode, the range, and the standard deviation to three significant figures.

4-6 The following measurements were made and tabulated by an engineer:

Class boundaries, in.	Frequency
4.35–4.45	1
4.45–4.55	4
4.55–4.65	7
4.65–4.75	15
4.75–4.85	11
4.85–4.95	10
4.95–5.05	2

Find the mean, the median, the mode, the range, and the class interval.

4-7 Draw a histogram for the data given in Prob. 4-8. Select the class interval to provide about 10 classes. List class boundaries.

4-8 The average delay time is being studied for a certain relay. The following two sets of data were collected on the time for the relay to close the contacts after receiving the proper impulse (testing was done with an oscilloscope):

Time, millisec	Time, millisec
2.45	2.47
2.57	2.58
2.76	2.62
2.56	2.72
2.72	2.66
2.63	2.61
2.61	2.58
2.70	2.72
2.51	2.63
2.65	2.57

Find the mean, the median, and the standard deviation of each set of data. Do the two sets appear to be uniform? Explain.

4-9 Twenty-five rivet heads drawn at random from a mass-production process have the following diameters, in centimeters:

2.54	2.53	2.53	2.54	2.57
2.53	2.52	2.54	2.54	2.53
2.54	2.54	2.55	2.53	2.55
2.55	2.56	2.52	2.51	2.54
2.55	2.53	2.56	2.53	2.54

Compute the mean to four significant figures, the median, the mode, the range, and the standard deviation. Use the short, or coding, method.

4-10 A room thermostat has been set to go on at $72°F$, and there have been some complaints that the room is too warm. To check the thermostat you bring in an accurate thermometer, attach a signal light to the thermostat, and take a temperature reading each time the light goes on. In one day you get the following 25 readings:

74	76	76	76	75
71	72	74	76	69
74	72	70	77	75
76	75	76	73	70
73	74	77	76	72

What is the average temperature? What is the standard deviation?

4-11 Prestressed concrete beams are tested to determine the load required to produce the first observable crack, and these load values are compared with values for beams of the same shape and total steel area designed with conventional reinforcing steel. The values recorded for the prestressed beams are

5.721	7.322	4.596	8.751
6.289	6.726	7.072	6.552
7.385	5.921	4.998	

The values recorded for the conventional beams are

3.716	4.219	5.161	4.582
3.991	2.970	4.012	3.766
4.211	3.225	3.721	4.721
3.277	3.862	3.762	4.217

Calculate the mean and standard deviation of the two sets of data.

4-12 A process for making electrical contacts is being evaluated. A study of the variation of one of the critical dimensions is made by taking a sample of 500 contacts, with the following results:

Class midpoint, in.	Frequency
0.215	3
0.220	16
0.225	66
0.230	90
0.235	109
0.240	91
0.245	73
0.250	35
0.255	15
0.260	2

Calculate the mean to four significant figures, the median, the mode, and the standard deviation to four significant figures.

4-13 The following four sets of data are obtained for the shear strength of stainless-steel spot welds 0.016 in. thick, where the strength is in pounds per weld:

146	162	150	148
148	160	144	154
146	146	152	152
140	156	154	152
150	150	138	154
146	146	154	154
146	154	160	158
142	150	160	158
152	148	152	156
148	148	150	160
158	148	150	162
152	150	150	154
146	152	152	148
156	150	158	152
152	152	152	148

150	152	156	158
150	152	156	162
146	148	152	160
148	152	154	160
152	146	154	158

Find $\bar{X}$ for each group and $\bar{X}$ for all four groups. Find σ_s for each group and σ_s for all four groups.

4-14 A laboratory study of the time delay in relay switches was as follows:

Time delay, sec	Frequency
0.120	1
0.125	3
0.130	8
0.135	15
0.140	23
0.145	15
0.150	8
0.155	3
0.160	1

Compute the mean and the standard deviation.

4-15 A city has available a maximum supply of 500,000 gal of water per day. An expansion of the average per capita consumption each month to the increased population expected in 5 years showed that in 5 years the requirements will be as follows:

Month	Consumption, gal	Month	Consumption, gal
January	327,000	July	576,000
February	422,000	August	588,000
March	421,000	September	582,000
April	478,000	October	472,000
May	521,000	November	452,000
June	558,000	December	421,000

Use a histogram to determine what percentage of the time the demand will exceed the supply. What can be done to alleviate the situation?

4-16   Operation times, in minutes, for work on a highway embankment were observed in several steps, as:

Loading (front-end loader)	Hauling	Spreading	Return
1.01	2.21	1.51	1.71
1.25	2.77	1.62	2.21
1.62	2.23	1.55	1.98
0.97	2.52	1.73	1.83
1.33	2.58	1.57	1.77
1.42	2.66	1.92	1.91
1.72	2.41	1.51	1.86
1.11	2.48	1.64	2.01
1.27	2.41	1.73	1.92
1.33	2.56	1.65	1.87
1.41	2.66	1.52	1.83

Calculate the mean and standard deviation for each step. Which steps are the most "stable"? Which are the most "variable"?

4-17   Assuming that the standard deviation of a sum is equal to the square root of the summation of the individual variances, use the data from Prob. 4-16 to calculate the standard deviation of the total trip time and compare this with the square root of the sum of the variances. (Note that the total trip time is not given.)

4-18   The following data were obtained in tests to determine the amount of tar in a certain brand of cigarettes:

X, mg	f	v'	fv'	fv'^2
12.0	3	-0.5	-1.5	0.75
12.1	10	-0.4	-4.0	1.60
12.2	14	-0.3	-4.2	1.26
12.3	19	-0.2	-3.8	0.76
12.4	27	-0.1	-2.7	0.27
12.5	39	0.0	0.0	0.00
12.6	50	0.1	5.0	0.50
12.7	32	0.2	6.4	1.28
12.8	20	0.3	6.0	1.80
12.9	13	0.4	5.2	2.08
13.0	3	0.5	1.5	0.75
	$\Sigma f = 230$		$\Sigma fv' = 7.9$	$\Sigma fv'^2 = 11.05$

Determine the arithmetic mean, the standard deviation, the median, and the mode.

4-19 The burning times of a liquid-fuel rocket propellant are as follows:

X, millisec	f
605	3
610	9
615	21
620	47
625	36
630	17
635	8
640	2
	$\Sigma f = 143$

Compute the arithmetic mean, the standard deviation, the median, and the mode.

five

normal distribution

Pacific Measurements

In Chapter Four we discussed descriptive methods of sample analysis for predicting the underlying characteristics of a population. In this chapter we will consider the *normal distribution* in some detail because of its importance in the area of measurements. As early as the eighteenth century scientists observed regularity in the distribution of measurements. A plot of the measurements showed a bell shape and was referred to in general as the *normal curve of errors*. The normal distribution also appears in mathematics with great frequency. The general form of the equation for normal distribution was developed by Carl Gauss (1777–1855) and sometimes is referred to as the *Gaussian distribution*. This functional relation is the basis of many statistical tables. If we denote the frequency of X_i as $f(X_i)$, then

$$f(X_i) = \frac{e^{[-\frac{1}{2}(X_i - \bar{X}_0)^2/\sigma_0^2]}}{\sigma_0 \sqrt{2\pi}} \qquad \textbf{5-1}$$

It is apparent that the frequency associated with each value of X_i is a function of the population mean $\bar{X}_0$ and the population standard deviation σ_0. In many cases the equation is written in a simpler form in terms of the parameters E_i and H, where

$$E_i = X_i - \bar{X}_0 \qquad \text{and} \qquad H = \frac{1}{\sqrt{2}\,\sigma_0}$$

Then Eq. 5-1 becomes

$$f(X_i) = \frac{H\,e^{-H^2 E_i^2}}{\sqrt{\pi}}$$

Note, however, that the frequency of X_i is still only a function of $\bar{X}_0$ and σ_0.

Once again we are confronted with the dilemma of defining $\bar{X}_0$ and σ_0 in order to use Eq. 5-1. We solve this problem by determining if our data generally correspond to the normal distribution. If it does, we then evaluate $\bar{X}$ and σ_s and use them in our process of statistical inference about the population. We determine if the data are reasonably defined by the normal distribution by inscribing a normal curve over a histogram of our data. The following is a description of a process to provide a normal curve consistent with our observed data, noting that all we can do is to judge how reasonable the fit is once we have completed the process.

First we define a new variable Z, which is the number of standard deviations that X_i is away from $\overline{X}_0$,

$$Z = \frac{X_i - \overline{X}_0}{\sigma_0} \qquad\qquad 5\text{-}2$$

This makes our plotting easier by providing a minimum number of points through which the curve must pass. Table 5-1 provides several values of frequency for Z_i

$$f(Z_i) = \frac{e^{-\frac{1}{2}Z_i^2}}{\sqrt{2\pi}}$$

which can then be used to produce the desired curve, where f is the ordinate value to the normal curve at each Z value. This is graphed in Fig. 5-1.

STD DEVIATION = 1.00

table 5-1   *Frequency of Z_i*

$\pm Z_i$	$f(Z_i)$
0.0	0.3989
0.5	0.3521
1.0	0.2420
1.5	0.1295
2.0	0.0540
3.0	0.0044
4.0	0.0001

figure 5-1

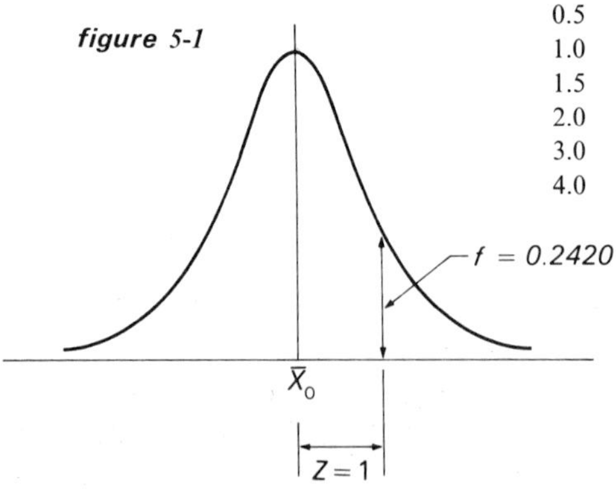

$f = 0.2420$

$\overline{X}_0$

$Z = 1$

Z = 1
(= THE POINT WHICH 1 STANDARD DEVIATION AWAY FROM THE MEAN).

Noting that

$$f(X_i) = \frac{f(Z_i)}{\sigma_0}$$

we can now evaluate points at various Z_i and place them on our histogram. The following equations provide the necessary plotting points:

$$f = \frac{\overline{f(Z_i)}nI}{\sigma_s} \qquad \text{(handwritten: } \text{Frequency} = \frac{\text{PROB } Z_i * n * I}{\sigma} \text{)} \qquad \text{5-3}$$

$$f_r = \frac{f(Z_i)I}{\sigma_s} \qquad\qquad\qquad \text{5-4}$$

where f = frequency   (handwritten: WHAT IS ?)

$\quad f_r$ = relative frequency

$\quad n$ = number of observations in sample

$\quad I$ = class interval

$$Z_i \simeq \frac{X_i - \overline{X}}{\sigma_s} \qquad (\text{we assume } \overline{X} \simeq \overline{X}_0)$$

$$X_i = \overline{X} \pm \sigma_s Z_i$$

Equation 5-3 is used when our histogram is frequency versus observed values of X_i, and Eq. 5-4 is used when the histogram is relative frequency versus observed values of X_i.

To illustrate this technique let us return once more to the data in Table 4-2 and Fig. 4-2. Note that we have already solved for $\overline{X}$ and σ_s, which are 19.96 and ± 1.60, respectively. Since Fig. 4-2 was plotted as frequency versus observed value, we use Eq. 5-3 to evaluate the plotting points, as shown in Table 5-2. If we plot this curve and superimpose it on the histogram of Fig. 4-2, we have the result shown in Fig. 5-2. It is apparent that the data are fairly close to a normal distribution, and we can be reasonably certain that the assumption of a normal distribution for our original population is valid.

EVALUATED from 2

table 5-2 Evaluation of plotting points	Z_i	X_i	$f(Z_i)$	$f(Z_i)nI/\sigma_s$
	3.0	24.76	0.0044	0.3
	2.0	23.16	0.0540	3.4
	1.5	22.36	0.1295	8.1
	1.0	21.56	0.2420	15.1
	0.5	20.76	0.3521	22.0
	0.0	19.96	0.3989	25.0
	−0.5	19.16	0.3521	22.0
	−1.0	18.36	0.2420	15.1
	−1.5	17.56	0.1295	8.1
	−2.0	16.76	0.0540	3.4
	−3.0	15.16	0.0044	0.3

Now that we are able to determine whether our data appear normally distributed, we can continue with our study of typical data that obey the normal distribution.

5-2 ACCURACY AND PRECISION AS RELATED TO THE NORMAL DISTRIBUTION

In Sec. 1-6 we discussed accuracy and precision; let us now relate these concepts to the normal-distribution function. We have just seen that the frequency or shape of the normal distribution is a function of the two parameters, $\overline{X}_0$ and σ_0. It is evident that $\overline{X}_0$ determines the midpoint of the bell curve and σ_0 determines the value of the ordinate as we move to either side of the midpoint. We thus conclude that the actual shape of the curve is a function of σ_0 and its location on the abscissa is a function of $\overline{X}_0$.

As was mentioned in Sec. 4-4, we rarely know the value of $\overline{X}_0$; hence we use $\overline{X}$ as its approximation, the difference being $\overline{E}$. Actually $\overline{E}$ is a measure of accuracy, as we are very close to the true value if $\overline{E}$ approaches zero, and we recall that $\overline{E}$ approaches zero if n is large. Although we can never know just what $\overline{E}$ is, we know that we can reduce $\overline{E}$ by increasing the sample size, provided all bias has been removed. In the marksmanship example in Sec. 1-6 we saw that the accuracy could be poor even when the precision was very good. This could be the result of a wind bias, or a sighting bias, or a combination of many such biases. We examine the sam-

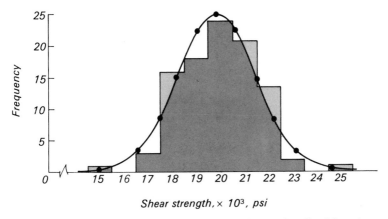

figure 5-2 *Normal-distribution curve superimposed on Fig. 4-2 to show relationship of data to normal distribution*

pling procedure for any cause of such bias before we attempt to increase accuracy through a large sample size.

As we have seen, precision can be observed even though the accuracy is not known. We now use σ_s as a measure of precision, with greater precision indicated by values of σ_s that approach zero. There is no way we can change the precision of data we have already observed, as its dispersion is a function of the distribution of the population from which we have taken the sample. However, a change in the precision of two samples taken at different times may indicate a change in the distribution of the population. Improved techniques in an industrial plant, for example, can change the distribution of a population, and a difference in the sample standard deviation could indicate that the new process was more precise than the old.

5-3 AREAS UNDER THE NORMAL-DISTRIBUTION CURVE

One of the most important properties of the normal-distribution function is that the area under the curve can be calculated between various points along the abscissa. Since the function is continuous between $\pm \infty$, we can use integral calculus to solve for the area. For a one-sided area

$$A_1 = \int \frac{e^{-Z^2/2}}{\sqrt{2\pi}}$$

and for a two-sided area

$$A_2 = 2 \int \frac{e^{-Z^2/2}}{\sqrt{2\pi}}$$

table 5-3 Area under the normal-distribution curve from Z to ∞	Z	Area (one side)	Area (two sides)
	0.0	0.5000	1.0000
	0.2	0.4207	0.8414
	0.4	0.3446	0.6892
	0.6	0.2743	0.5486
	0.8	0.2119	0.4238
	1.0	0.1587	0.3174
	1.2	0.1151	0.2302
	1.4	0.0808	0.1616
	1.6	0.0548	0.1096
	1.8	0.0359	0.0718
	2.0	0.0228	0.0456
	2.5	0.0062	0.0124
	3.0	0.0014	0.0028
	3.5	0.0002	0.0004

table 5-4 Area under the normal-distribution curve from X_0 to Z	Z	Area (one side)	Area (two sides)
	0.0	0.0000	0.0000
	0.2	0.0793	0.1586
	0.4	0.1554	0.3108
	0.6	0.2257	0.4514
	0.8	0.2881	0.5762
	1.0	0.3413	0.6826
	1.2	0.3849	0.7698
	1.4	0.4192	0.8384
	1.6	0.4452	0.8904
	1.8	0.4641	0.9282
	2.0	0.4772	0.9544
	2.5	0.4938	0.9876
	3.0	0.4987	0.9974
	3.5	0.4998	0.9996

This area is used universally, and most books of tables include it. The complete tables are given in Appendix G; portions are shown here as Tables 5-3 and 5-4. These tables are based on our previous definition of the function Z, the number of standard deviations from the mean.

The tables are used to determine the area under the curves between different limits, as illustrated in Figs. 5-3 and 5-4. The area under the curve is actually the probability that events in the shaded areas will occur. This is because the total area under the curve is 1, and we are dealing with a portion of a unit area. Suppose we want to know what percentage of the area under a normal-

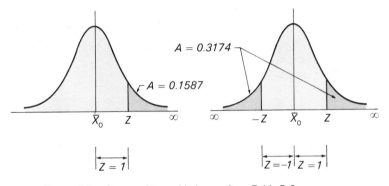

figure 5-3   One- and two-sided areas from Table 5-3

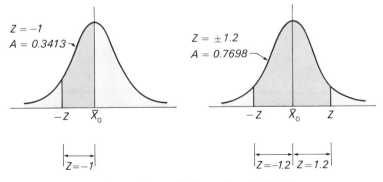

figure 5-4   One- and two-sided areas from Table 5-4

distribution curve is found between $(+ -)$ one standard deviation. The two-sided portion of Table 5-4 provides the numerical value of 68.26 percent.

Let us now consider additional examples of the use of these tables. Note that most references are to either Table 5-3 or Table 5-4, as all problems can be worked from either table. Both have been provided to make the problem solving easier and because the area may be presented differently in other books. Care should be taken in using other statistical tables from other texts to determine the form of the table.

> ***example 5-1*** A firm is manufacturing ball bearings for a precision tool maker who specifies that the individual balls are to be graded such that those he receives are 0.500 ± 0.005 in. diameter. Several samples of 100 balls have been taken, and the results are $\overline{X} = 0.5000$ in. and $\sigma_s = 0.00312$ in. What percentage of the balls will be rejected with these criteria?

> We will solve this problem by means of both tables. First we draw a picture which represents the problem, and then we obtain the necessary data from the table. From the shaded area of our picture, Fig. 5-5, we see that the area is given by Table 5-3 (two sides) as 0.1096. Therefore the percentage of rejects is 10.96 percent. We can also solve this problem by means of Table 5-4, which gives us the unshaded area. In this case the percentage of rejects is 1 minus the value from the table,

> $1 - 0.8904 = 0.1096$, or 10.96 percent

> ***example 5-2*** Consider the basic data from Example 5-1, except that now $\overline{X} = 0.502$ and $\sigma_s = 0.0050$ in. Note that this situation, where the sample mean and the specified mean value do not agree, is the more usual case.

> We start with a graphic representation of the problem, shown in Fig. 5-6. We first note that the area is not symmetrical,

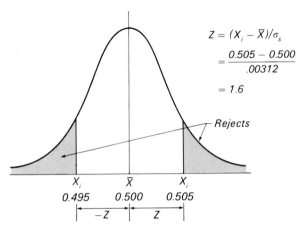

$$Z = (X_i - \bar{X})/\sigma_s$$
$$= \frac{0.505 - 0.500}{.00312}$$
$$= 1.6$$

figure 5-5

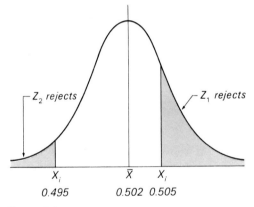

figure 5-6

$$Z_1 = \frac{0.505 - 0.502}{0.005} = 0.6 \qquad Z_2 = \frac{0.495 - 0.502}{0.005} = -1.4$$

Therefore we cannot use the two-sided portion of the tables. From Table 5-3,

$$A = 0.2743 + 0.0808 = 0.3551, \text{ or } 35.51 \text{ percent rejects}$$

From Table 5-4, the area not shaded is $0.2257 + 0.4192 = 0.6449$. Hence

$1 - 0.6449 = 0.3551$, or 35.51 percent rejects.

example 5-3 For a shaft to fit freely into a piece of machinery it has been specified that the maximum acceptable shaft diameter is 2.005 in. The shafts produced by a certain process have been reviewed, and the results are $\overline{X} = 1.998$ and $\sigma_s = 0.0035$. What percentage of the shafts are acceptable?

Using Table 5-3, we would solve for the unshaded area in Fig. 5-7 and subtract it from 1:

$A = 1 - 0.0228 = 0.9772$, or 97.72 percent acceptable

Using Table 5-4, we would solve for the shaded areas, noting that the left half is 0.5000:

$A = 0.5000 + 0.4772 = 0.9772$, or 97.72 percent acceptable

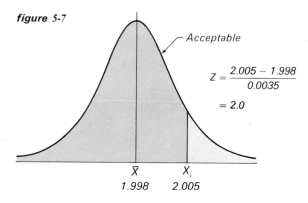

figure 5-7

$$Z = \frac{2.005 - 1.998}{0.0035}$$

$$= 2.0$$

Acceptable

$\overline{X}$ X_i
1.998   2.005

example 5-4 In a manufacturing process the time required to complete a certain electronic component has been studied, with the results $\overline{X} = 2$ hr and $\sigma_s = 8$ min. The company is in the process of negotiating a contract with the union and wishes to establish a standard time for producing this component such that 90 percent of the components currently being produced are completed within this time or sooner.

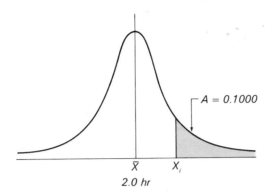

2.0 hr

figure 5-8

We will use only Table 5-3 for this solution, but either table could be used. The problem is to find a Z such that the shaded area in Fig. 5-8 is 0.1000. From Table 5-3 we find that Z is between 1.2 and 1.4, and by interpolation we obtain the following:

$$Z = 1.2 + 0.2 \times \frac{151}{343} = 1.288 \text{ min}$$

where we obtained the last part of the expression by the procedure

$$(1.4 - 1.2) \times \frac{0.1151 - 0.1000}{0.1151 - 0.0808}$$

(If we use the complete table in the appendix, less interpolation is necessary, and the value is 1.282.) Now that we know Z, we can solve for X_i:

$$Z = \frac{X_i - \overline{X}}{\sigma_s} \qquad X_i = \overline{X} + \sigma_s Z$$

$$X_i = 2.0 + \frac{8}{60} \times 1.288 = 2.0 + 0.172 = 2.172 \text{ hr}$$

or

$$X_i = 2 \text{ hr} + 8 \times 1.288 \text{ min} = 2 \text{ hr } 10 \text{ min}$$

5-4   THE STANDARD ERROR OF THE MEAN

Let us take m samples of size n from a population and then use the means of each of these samples as a secondary sample. We make the assumption that all the $\overline{X}_i$ have the same expected value and can be considered to be the same in our equations. Although this is not strictly true, it is a valid assumption, since all the $\overline{X}_i$ are very close to the same value. First let us define two new terms.

If we denote $\overline{X}_i$ as

$$\overline{X}_i = \frac{\sum_{j=1}^{n} X_{ij}}{n}$$

where i is the ith sample and j is the jth observation in the ith sample, then we may define the *mean of means* as

$$\overline{\overline{X}} = \frac{\sum_{i=1}^{m} \overline{X}_i}{m} \simeq \frac{m\overline{X}}{m} \simeq \overline{X} \qquad 5\text{-}5$$

where

$$\overline{X} = \overline{X}_1, \overline{X}_2, \ldots, \overline{X}_m = \text{constant}$$

The term for the variance would be of the form

$$\sigma_m{}^2 = \frac{\sum_{i=1}^{m} (\overline{X}_i - \overline{\overline{X}})^2}{m} = \frac{\sum_{i=1}^{m} \left(\dfrac{\sum_{j=1}^{n} X_{ij}}{n} - \overline{\overline{X}} \right)^2}{m}$$

An expansion beyond the scope of this text yields an approximation of the *standard deviation of means*,

$$\sigma_m = \frac{\sigma_0}{\sqrt{n}} \simeq \frac{\sqrt{(n-1)/n}\,\sigma_s}{\sqrt{n}} \simeq \frac{\sqrt{n-1}\,\sigma_s}{n} \simeq \frac{\sigma_s}{\sqrt{n}} \qquad 5\text{-}6$$

The term σ_m is often referred to as the *standard error of the mean* or

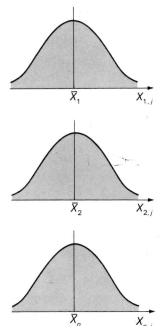

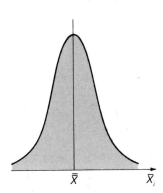

figure 5-9   *Relationship of individual sample means to the mean of a sample made of the individual mean values*

simply *standard error*. This approximation is valid only when the sample size is large, say $n > 30$.

Let us look at a graphical representation of this process to see whether it seems reasonable. Figure 5-9 shows that only the mean values are used at data points in the sample of means. We would expect a great deal less dispersion in a sample made up of mean values, all of which are considered an approximation of $\overline{X}_0$. Therefore we would assume $\sigma_m < \sigma_0$. This relation is also called the *central-limit theorem*.

5-5   CONFIDENCE LIMITS

We now have developed the necessary background to discuss the use of the mean and the standard deviation for estimating.

Since we are usually unable to evaluate $\overline{X}_0$ and σ_0, how reliable are our estimates? One of the most important single determinants is the sampling technique itself. If care is not taken to ensure a random sample, all our conclusions thus far are invalid, and the reasoning that follows would not apply. Let us assume here that we do have a random sample.   :

If we are asked for a single estimate of $\overline{X}_0$, we must use the best data at hand. If we have taken many samples, then the best estimate would be

$$\overline{\overline{X}} = \frac{\sum\limits_{i=1}^{m} \overline{X}_i}{m}$$

where m is the number of samples taken. If we do not have extensive data available, then we must use a single $\overline{X}$ as our estimator. Generally we try to establish two limiting values between which we expect $\overline{X}_0$ to lie. These limits are $-\infty$ and $+\infty$ in normally distributed data, but from a practical standpoint they are unrealistic. We then return to the implication in Table 5-3 that there is a certain amount of area left in the "tails" of the curve between $\pm Z$ standard deviations. Our goal is to establish a set of limits between which we expect $\overline{X}_0$ to lie with a given probability. To do this we must establish what probability of error we are willing to accept. For example, where human life is involved we insist on a very low probability of error, while in other instances we can accept greater probability of error. The probability of error that we will accept is actually the area remaining in the tails of the normal curve, as shown in Fig. 5-10.

The process of obtaining the range of $\overline{X}_0$ entails first a judgment of the acceptable probability of error. We then define our *level of confidence*, or *degree of confidence*, as 1 minus this probability of error. Equations 5-7 to 5-9 employ a value of Z which is obtained directly from this acceptable probability of error. Since we wish to estimate the accuracy of our mean, we assume a distribution of means as our base and thus use σ_m and $\overline{\overline{X}}$ (in reality it may be necessary to use $\overline{X}$ as an estimate of $\overline{\overline{X}}$ and $\sigma_s/\sqrt{n}$ as an estimate of σ_m). Thus the range for $\overline{X}_0$ is defined as

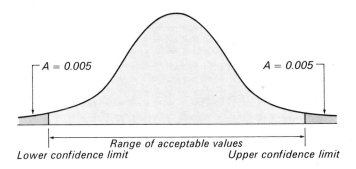

Range of acceptable values

Lower confidence limit   Upper confidence limit

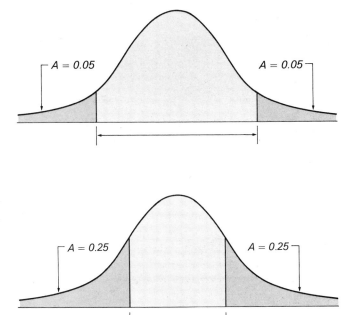

figure 5-10   Relationship of acceptable error to range of acceptable values

Z	One-sided confidence, %	Two-sided confidence, %
0.842	80	60
1.00	84.2	68.3
1.282	90	80
1.645	95	90
1.960(2.0)	97.5	95
2.326	99	98
2.576	99.5	99

table 5-5   Values of Z used with confidence limits

$$(\overline{X}_0) = \overline{\overline{X}} \pm Z\sigma_m \qquad \text{with } 1 - A_{z_2} \text{ level of confidence} \qquad \textbf{5-7}$$

where the upper limit is

$$U(\overline{X}_0) = \overline{\overline{X}} + Z\sigma_m \qquad \text{with } 1 - A_{z_1} \text{ level of confidence} \qquad \textbf{5-8}$$

and the lower limit is

$$L(\overline{X}_0) = \overline{\overline{X}} - Z\sigma_m \qquad \text{with } 1 - A_{z_1} \text{ level of confidence} \qquad \textbf{5-9}$$

In the development of confidence limits special values of Z are often used. These are summarized in Table 5-5.

Now for a few examples.

example 5-5   A spot speed check was made on a main city street to determine the average speed of drivers, with the results $\overline{X} = 31$ mph, $n = 100$, and $\sigma_s = 2$ mph. Is it possible that the average speed could actually be as low as 30 mph (the posted speed limit)? Use a 95 percent confidence limit.

We are asked to test only for a lower limit, and not to find a range, so we use Eq. 5-9. A graphic representation of the problem is shown in Fig. 5-11. Table 5-5 for a one-sided confidence test gives $Z = 1.645$ at 95 percent confidence. Note that this implies that there is 5 percent of the area under the curve remaining in the tail.

$$L(\overline{X}_0) = \overline{\overline{X}} - Z\sigma_m = 31 - 1.645 \times \frac{2}{\sqrt{100}}$$

$$= 31 - 0.33 = 30.67 \text{ mph with 95 percent confidence}$$

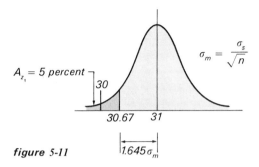

figure 5-11

Since we are 95 percent confident that the real $\overline{X}_0$ is greater than 30.67 mph, we can conclude that the actual average speed is greater than the posted limit of 30 mph.

example 5-6   The following data were taken from water samples for a proposed backup source of water. Average hardness was 76 mg/liter and standard deviation was 20 mg/liter. If an acceptance test requires that the maximum average hardness be less than 81 mg/liter at the 97.5 percent confidence level, would the source be acceptable if n had been 25? If n had been 100?

We use Eq. 5-8, since we are considering the upper limit only. Thus for $n = 25$

$$U(\overline{X}_0) = \overline{X} + Z\sigma_m = \overline{X} + Z\frac{\sigma_s}{\sqrt{n}}$$

$$= 76 + 2.0 \times \frac{20}{\sqrt{25}} = 84 \text{ mg/liter}$$

Since the population could have an average hardness of 84, we would conclude that it fails the test. We may choose to resample, since our sample size was so small, or we may look for an alternate source of water. This is a decision that would be made in real life after a complete study of all possibilities.

For $n = 100$

$$U(\overline{X}_0) = 76 + 2.0 \times \frac{20}{\sqrt{100}} = 76 + 4 = 80 \text{ mg/liter}$$

With σ_s still at 20 and the sample size 100, the results would show the potential supply as acceptable.

Example 5-6 is not just a manipulation of data to reach a desired end, but rather an indication that statistical theory is based on the laws of probability. When fewer observations are taken, our statistical inference is more conservative, since we are less certain of the accuracy of our data.

example 5-7   To determine a statistical range for the mean of a certain industrial process it was decided to evaluate the 99 percent confidence limits. The data obtained from observing 144 items were $\overline{X} = 105.2$ lb and $\sigma_s = 25.4$ lb. What is the range?

We now use Eq. 5-7, since we have a two-sided test on confidence limits. Thus

$$R(\overline{X}_0) = \overline{\overline{X}} \pm Z\sigma_m \simeq \overline{X} \pm Z \frac{\sigma_s}{\sqrt{n}}$$

$$= 105.2 \pm 2.576 \times \frac{25.4}{12}$$

with the upper and lower limits

$$U(\overline{X}_0) = 110.7 \qquad L(\overline{X}_0) = 99.7$$

Hence the range is

$$R(\overline{X}_0) = 110.7 - 99.7 = 11.0$$

Note that

$$R = 2\left(Z \frac{\sigma_s}{\sqrt{n}}\right) = 11.0$$

By now it should be apparent that the problem in establishing confidence limits is that our restriction to a narrow range of acceptable values produces a greater probability of error, whereas our goal is a small probability of error.

5-6 *THE DIFFERENCE OF MEANS*

We frequently measure a physical process over a period of time. One goal may be to determine whether the process is constant or changes with time. There are various ways of testing for this, and one of the simplest is taking the *difference of means*. Before we consider the technique of this process let us define the necessary equations for evaluating the difference of means. For two different sets of data, which we will refer to as set 1 and set 2, let

$$X_{(1-2)_i} = X_{1_i} - X_{2_i}$$

where X_1 is set 1 and X_2 is set 2. From Eq. 4-2 we have

$$\overline{X} = \frac{\sum_{i=1}^{n} X_i}{n}$$

and substitution yields

$$\overline{X}_{1-2} = \frac{\sum_{i=1}^{n} X_{1_i} - X_{2_i}}{n}$$

then

$$n\overline{X}_{1-2} = \sum_{i=1}^{n} (X_{1_i} - X_{2_i}) = \sum_{i=1}^{n} X_{1_i} - \sum_{i=1}^{n} X_{2_i}$$

or

$$\overline{X}_{1-2} = \frac{\sum_{i=1}^{n} X_{1_i}}{n_1} - \frac{\sum_{i=1}^{n} X_{2_i}}{n_2} \qquad \text{where } n_1 = n_2$$

Hence

$$\overline{X}_{1-2} = \overline{X}_1 - \overline{X}_2 \qquad \qquad \textbf{\textit{5-10}}$$

This is the mean of the difference between samples from sets 1 and 2.

Next let us develop an expression for σ^2_{1-2}, the variance of the difference between samples from sets 1 and 2. We express the variance as (see Sec. 4-7)

$$\sigma^2 = \frac{\sum\limits_{i=1}^{n} (X_i - \overline{X})^2}{n}$$

and substitution for X_i and $\overline{X}$ gives us

$$\sigma^2_{1-2} = \frac{\sum\limits_{i=1}^{n} [(X_{1_i} - X_{2_i}) - (\overline{X}_1 - \overline{X}_2)]^2}{n}$$

or

$$n\sigma^2_{1-2} = \sum\limits_{i=1}^{n} [(X_{1_i} - X_{2_i}) - (\overline{X}_1 - \overline{X}_2)]^2$$

$$= \sum\limits_{i=1}^{n} [(X_{1_i} - \overline{X}_1) - (X_{2_i} - \overline{X}_2)]^2$$

If we let

$$a_i = (X_{1_i} - \overline{X}_1) \qquad b_i = (X_{2i} - \overline{X}_2)$$

then

$$n\sigma^2_{1-2} = \sum\limits_{i=1}^{n} (a_i - b_i)^2 = \sum\limits_{i=1}^{n} (a_i^2 - 2a_ib_i + b_i^2)$$

$$= \sum\limits_{i=1}^{n} a_i^2 + \sum\limits_{i=1}^{n} b_i^2 - 2 \sum\limits_{i=1}^{n} (a_ib_i)$$

and substituting again for a_i and b_i gives us

$$n\sigma^2_{1-2} = \sum_{i=1}^{n} (X_{1_i} - \bar{X}_1)^2 + \sum_{i=1}^{n} (X_{2_i} - \bar{X}_2)^2$$

$$- 2 \sum_{i=1}^{n} (X_{1_i} - \bar{X}_1)(X_{2_i} - \bar{X}_2)$$

From Eq. 4-3,

$$\sum_{i=1}^{n} (X_i - \bar{X}) = 0$$

Therefore the last term goes to zero, leaving

$$n\sigma^2_{1-2} = \sum_{i=1}^{n} (X_{1_i} - \bar{X}_1)^2 + \sum_{i=1}^{n} (X_{2_i} - \bar{X}_2)^2$$

or

$$\sigma^2_{1-2} = \frac{\sum_{i=1}^{n} (X_{1_i} - \bar{X}_1)^2}{n} + \frac{\sum_{i=1}^{n} (X_{2_i} - \bar{X}_2)^2}{n}$$

Thus the variance of the difference between samples from sets 1 and 2 is

$$\sigma^2_{1-2} = \sigma_1{}^2 + \sigma_2{}^2 \qquad\qquad \textbf{5-11}$$

and the standard deviation of the difference is

$$\sigma_{1-2} = \sqrt{\sigma_1{}^2 + \sigma_2{}^2} \qquad\qquad \textbf{5-12}$$

The fact that the variance of the difference of two sets of data is actually the sum of the individual variances will be discussed further in Chapter Six and is expanded more fully in Appendix E.

When we compare means, what we are really testing is the hypothesis that they are from the same population. We do this by combining the confidence-limit concept with the difference equations we have just developed. If we compare the means of two samples taken by the same process, we assume that their difference will lie within certain limits if they are actually from the same population and will lie outside these limits if they are from different populations. Consider that for two different populations

$$\bar{X}_{0_1} = \bar{\bar{X}}_1 \pm Z\sigma_{m_1} \qquad \bar{X}_{0_2} = \bar{\bar{X}}_2 \pm Z\sigma_{m_2}$$

If we assume that the two sets of data are from the same population, then $\bar{\bar{X}}_1 - \bar{\bar{X}}_2$ approaches zero, and the limits of $\bar{X}_{0_{1-2}}$ are given by

$$R(\bar{X}_{0_{1-2}}) = \bar{\bar{X}}_{1-2} \pm Z\sigma_{m_{1-2}} = 0 \pm Z\sigma_{m_{1-2}} \qquad \textbf{5-13}$$

where we have used the form of Eq. 5-7 to predict the mean difference of means.

We also need an expression for $\sigma_{m_{1-2}}$. From the relationships developed previously,

$$n\sigma_m^2 = \sigma_0^2$$

and

$$\sigma_m = \frac{\sigma_0}{\sqrt{n}}$$

It follows by substitution that

$$n\sigma_{m_{1-2}}^2 = \sigma_{1-2}^2$$

and

$$\sigma_{m_{1-2}}^2 = \frac{\sigma_{1-2}^2}{n}$$

Hence

$$\sigma_{m_{1-2}}^2 = \frac{\sigma_1^2}{n_1} + \frac{\sigma_2^2}{n_2}$$

and

$$\sigma_{m_{1-2}} = \sqrt{\frac{\sigma_1^2}{n_1} + \frac{\sigma_2^2}{n_2}}$$

Although we have restricted our considerations so far to a comparison of the same process over time, the difference of means can also be used to test averages of different processes. Note however, that in problems where we limited ourselves to one process the standard deviation tended to remain fairly constant over time; this is not the case in comparing different processes. Hence the knowledge that the means of the two processes could be from the same population may not be the only criterion for decision making; advanced texts on statistics provide many more tools to help in this case.

Let us now consider some examples of these two basic types of problems.

example 5-8 Residents on a certain city street reported that the traffic past their homes on Friday afternoons greatly exceeded the speed limit (25 mph) and was a hazard to their children. Previous spot checks made with radar on a typical day had shown the average speed to be 24.7 mph with a standard deviation of 2.6 mph. In order to pacify the residents, a spot check was made on a Friday afternoon, with the results $\overline{X} = 26.3$ mph and $\sigma_s = 3.2$ mph. If all sample sizes $n = 25$, what would you tell the city engineer regarding a significant difference in the average speed Friday afternoons? Would sample sizes of $n = 100$ change your answer?

Assume that the differences measured are just the result of two different samples from the same population. We use Eq. 5-13 to find limits for $\overline{X}_{1-2}$, and if the actual difference is greater we will assume that the average speeds are from a different population. Setting the confidence level at 95 percent for this solution, we have a range of

$$R(X_{0_{1-2}}) = \pm Z\sigma_{m_{1-2}} = \pm Z \sqrt{\frac{\sigma_1^{2}}{n} + \frac{\sigma_2^{2}}{n}}$$

$$= \pm 2 \sqrt{\frac{2.6^2}{25} + \frac{3.2^2}{25}} = \pm 2 \sqrt{\frac{6.76 + 12.4}{25}}$$

$$= \pm 2 \times 0.778^{\frac{1}{2}} = \pm 1.75 \text{ mph}$$

The actual difference between the speed on Friday and that on a typical day is

$$\overline{X}_{1-2} = \overline{X}_1 - \overline{X}_2 = 24.7 - 26.3 = -1.6 \text{ mph}$$

and since -1.6 lies within the bounds of ± 1.75 mph, we assume that there is no significant difference at the 95 percent confidence level for samples of 25.

For samples of 100

$$R(X_{0_{1-2}}) = \pm 2\sqrt{\frac{2.6^2}{100} + \frac{3.2^2}{100}} = \pm 2\sqrt{\frac{19.16}{100}}$$

$$= \pm 2 \times 0.1916^{\frac{1}{2}} = \pm 0.88 \text{ mph}$$

Since -1.6 is greater than the limits ± 0.88, we assume that the average speed on Friday afternoons is actually greater than that on a typical day.

example 5-9 A company producing lead batteries for cars feels that their quality control improves their product. To back up this statement they quote the following statistics, noting that production has been the same for 10 years except for the addition of a quality-control section:

	Expected life, months	Average life 100 samples, months	Standard error of means
Five years ago	24	27.3	1.8
Today	24	30.1	1.6

Do you feel that there has been a significant change in the product?

From Eq. 5-13, the limits at a 95 percent confidence level are

$$R(\overline{X}_{0_{1-2}}) = \pm Z\sigma_{m_{1-2}} = \pm 2\sqrt{1.8^2 + 1.6^2}$$

$$= \pm 2\sqrt{5.8} = \pm 2 \times 2.4$$

$$= \pm 4.8 \text{ months}$$

Actually,

$$\bar{X}_1 - \bar{X}_2 = 27.3 - 30.1 = 2.8 \text{ months}$$

Since 2.8 lies within the limits of ± 4.8 months, we can conclude that there has been no significant change in the product.

example 5-10 A racing driver is selecting a fuel to use in competition and has narrowed his selection down to two fuels. From the following data, which fuel should he use?

	Average miles/gal in his car	Standard deviation miles/gal	Sample size
Brand X	8.3	1.2	20
Brand Y	9.2	2.1	20

The limits at a 95 percent confidence level are

$$R(\bar{X}_{0_{1-2}}) = \pm Z\sigma_{m_{1-2}} = \pm 2\sqrt{\frac{2.1^2 + 1.2^2}{20}}$$

$$= \pm 2\sqrt{0.293} = \pm 1.08 \text{ miles/gal}$$

The actual difference is

$$9.2 - 8.3 = 0.9 \text{ mile/gal}$$

Since the 0.9 mile/gal lies within the limits of ± 1.08 miles/gal, it appears that there is no significant difference in the fuels. Note, however, that brand Y has a greater standard deviation, which is not as desirable; the driver may want to make additional tests before making a selection.

5-7 DETERMINATION OF SAMPLE SIZE

Since sample sizes are used in problems relating to statistical inference, how do we know how big to make the sample to obtain desirable results? In general, statisticians consider $n = 25$ a minimum sample for making a valid statistical inference. However, let us look into this matter a bit further. As in any other situation, the problem is easier if we have some knowledge of the population with which we are dealing. Let us first consider the case where the population is normally distributed and we have some knowledge of the variation. Later we will relax this process and discuss a procedure that can be used with no knowledge at all of the underlying distribution.

Assume that we have some previous sample whose plot implied a normal distribution and whose size was large enough to give a reasonable σ_s. If

$$\overline{X}_0 \simeq \overline{X} \pm Z\sigma_m$$

then, from the last term of this expression, the range is

$$R \simeq 2Z\sigma_m \simeq 2Z \frac{\sigma'_s}{\sqrt{n}}$$

where σ'_s is from our previous sample. Thus the sample size necessary to set the confidence limits in a predetermined range can be approximated from

$$\sqrt{n} \simeq \frac{2Z\sigma'_s}{R}$$

or

$$n \simeq \left(\frac{2Z\sigma'_s}{R}\right)^2 \qquad \qquad \textit{5-14}$$

example 5-11 How large a sample is necessary to set the 95 percent confidence limits on the true mean at ± 0.1 in. if a previous sample of 30 gave $\sigma_s = 0.5$ in?

From Eq. 5-14,

$$n = \left(\frac{2Z\sigma'_s}{R}\right)^2 = \left(\frac{2.0 \times 2.0 \times 0.5}{0.2}\right)^2 = 10^2 = 100$$

The second type of problem where no knowledge is available

about the general underlying distribution can be solved by a theorem known as *Chebyshev's inequality*,

$$P(|\overline{X} - \overline{X}_0| > k\sigma) < \frac{1}{k^2} \qquad \textbf{5-15}$$

(for a proof of this theorem see any advanced text on statistics). This theorem states that a unit area under the curve of a distribution that is k standard deviations from the mean is smaller than $1/k^2$. For example, for a known normal distribution, the area (two sides) that is two standard deviations from the mean is less than $(1/2)^2$, or 0.25. Referring to Table 5-3, we see that it is actually 0.0456, which is less than 0.25. We can use Eq. 5-15 to determine a sample size when we have no previous knowledge, but it results in very large samples. If the cost of sampling is significant, it may be more practical to determine the sample size in some other way.

Note that the expression $P(|\overline{X} - \overline{X}_0| > k\sigma)$ in Eq. 5-15 is the same thing as the area associated with Z_i. Hence for a two-sided area we may write

$$A_2 < \frac{1}{k^2} \qquad \textbf{5-16}$$

Then the range is

$$R = \pm \frac{k\sigma}{\sqrt{n}} = 2\left| \frac{k\sigma}{\sqrt{n}} \right|$$

or

$$\sqrt{n} = \frac{2k\sigma}{R}$$

We now need to state R in terms of σ in order to obtain a cancellation. We let

$$R = C\sigma$$

or

$$C = \frac{R}{\sigma}$$

Then, by substitution

$$n = \frac{4k^2\sigma^2}{C^2\sigma^2} = \frac{4k^2}{C^2}$$

and if we define the area as

$$A = \frac{1}{k^2}$$

we may write

$$n = \frac{4}{C^2 A} \qquad \qquad \textbf{5-17}$$

We now need to state the range as a function of the standard deviation, which we do not yet know.

example 5-12 What sample size would be necessary to provide a 95 percent confidence level when the true mean is to be found within $\pm\sigma/2$ from the sample mean?

Note that since

$$R = 2\left|\frac{\sigma}{2}\right| = \sigma$$

we have $C = 1$. Thus for the given confidence level

$$A = 1 - 0.95 = 0.05$$

and

$$n = \frac{4}{1 \times 0.05} = 80$$

example 5-13 What would be the necessary sample size to find $\overline{X}_0$ within ± 0.01, with 90 percent confidence?

Since

$$R = 2 \times 0.01\sigma$$

the cancellation is $C = 0.02$. Hence

$A = 1 - 0.9 = 0.1$

and

$$n = \frac{4}{0.1 \times 0.02} = \frac{4}{0.002} = 2{,}000$$

SUMMARY

The normal-distribution curve describes the probability distribution of most engineering measurements. Because of their great importance, the areas under this curve have been tabulated to facilitate probability calculations. These tabulations are presented as the area between a specific value on the abscissa and positive infinity and as the area between the mean and a specific value on the abscissa. Care must be taken to select the table that is applicable to the problem.

In making predictions about a mean of a population we utilize a distribution made up of means of samples taken from the population. This distribution provides us with a mean of means $\overline{\overline{X}}$ and a standard deviation of means σ_m, which we use to make predictions, in the form of confidence limits, about the population mean.

The relation between the standard deviation of a sample and the standard deviation of the means allows us to establish a sample size to obtain desirable results.

PROBLEMS

5-1 Assume that the histogram you drew for Prob. 4-7 represents normally distributed data. Test this assumption by inscribing a normal curve over the histogram.

5-2 The average annual rainfall in a certain town is 34.0 in., with a standard deviation of 3.0 in. Assuming a normal distribution, in how many years in a 40-year period would you expect 28.0 to 40.0 in. of rain?

5-3 The average grade on an examination was 73 percent, and the standard deviation was 8.0 percent. All students who scored between 65 and 81 percent were assigned a grade of C. If 35 students got a C, how many students took the examination? Assume a normal distribution.

5-4 A random sample was taken of the diameters of machine shafts produced by a manufacturing firm, with the results $\overline{X} = 1.575$ in. and $\sigma_s = 0.0055$ in. If shafts having diameters between 1.5622 and 1.5838 in. are considered acceptable, what is the percentage of rejects?

5-5 Studies indicate that the average life of a certain make of automobile battery is 36 months, with a standard deviation of 5 months. Assuming a normal distribution, what percentage of these batteries can be expected to last 28 to 44 months?

5-6 The average life of a television picture tube is 4.7 years, with $\sigma_s = 1.5$ years. If the manufacturer guarantees free replacement of any tubes that last less than 2.0 years, how many tubes will have to be replaced free out of a production of 2,000 tubes?

5-7 Specifications for a certain electric circuit will allow relay switches that function within 0.154 sec. Study of a random sample of 77 relay switches showed $\overline{X} = 0.140$ sec and $\sigma_s = 0.0078$ sec. What percentage of the switches are acceptable?

5-8 The variation of one of the critical dimensions in a part is studied by taking a random sample of 50 from the 10,000 parts produced per day, with the results $\overline{X} = 0.2363$ in. and $\sigma_s = 0.00867$ in. How many parts would have dimensions between 0.2276 and 0.2450 in. at the end of one week's production (5 days)? If dimensions outside the range of 0.2189 to 0.2537 in. are not acceptable, how many parts would be rejected in one week's production?

5-9 One thousand electric light bulbs are tested, and it is found that they have an average life of 950 hr, with a standard deviation of 150 hr. If we assume a normal distribution, how many bulbs may be expected to have a life of 800 to 1,100 hr? A life of less than 650 hr? A life of 1,100 to 1,250 hr?

5-10 A study showed that the life of a certain vacuum tube is normally distributed, with a mean of 1,880 days and a standard deviation of 220 days. If the manufacturer wishes to guarantee the tube for 48 months (a month is taken to be 30 days), what percentage of the tubes will he have to replace under the guarantee?

5-11 One thousand resistors were tested and found to have an average resistance of 300 ohms, with a standard deviation of 30 ohms. Assuming a normal distribution, how many of the resistors may be expected to have a resistance of 270 to 360 ohms? A resistance of 330 to 360 ohms? A resistance of less than 240 ohms? If 90 percent of the resistors were found satisfactory for a certain task, what limits would you set to determine their acceptability?

5-12 The manufacturer of some electrical resistors has set 47.8 ohms as the lower limit of acceptability for his product. If the quality is maintained such that no more than 5.0 percent of the production is likely to be defective because of low resistance, if the distribution is normal, and if the standard deviation is 1.7 ohms, what is the mean resistance?

5-13 The following velocities of jet aircraft were observed at the end of a catapult on an aircraft carrier:

X, knots	f
135	5
140	6
145	13
150	8
155	17
160	14
165	7
170	1

Find the mean, the standard deviation, the median, and the standard error of the mean. Within what limits would 90 percent of the velocities fall?

5-14 The ages of a group of children are as follows:

Age, years	f
2	1
4	3
6	4
8	7
10	5
12	2
14	2

Calculate the mean, the standard deviation, the standard error of the mean, the range, the median, and the mode.

5-15 The following temperatures were taken in a kiln:

$X, °F$	f	v'	fv'	fv'^2
130	1	−20	−20	400
135	5	−15	−75	1,125
140	6	−10	−60	600
145	13	−5	−65	325
150	8	0	0	0
155	17	5	85	425
160	14	10	140	1,400
165	7	15	105	1,575
170	1	20	20	400
175	3	25	75	1,875
	$\Sigma f = 75$		$\Sigma fv' = 205$	$\Sigma fv'^2 = 8,125$

Find the mean, the standard deviation, the median, and the standard error of the mean.

5-16 The following burning times of a solid-fuel rocket are given:

$X, million$	f
35.1	3
35.3	8
35.5	17
35.7	29
35.9	22
36.1	9
36.3	4
36.5	2

Find the mean, the standard deviation, the median, and the standard error of the mean. Within what limits would 50 percent of the burning times fall?

5-17 A study has indicated that the life of a certain kind of automobile battery is normally distributed, with a mean of 1,380 days and a standard deviation of 150 days. If the manufacturer wishes to guarantee the battery for 36 months (a month is taken to be 30 days), what percentage of the batteries will he have to replace under the guarantee? Within what limits would the life of 50 percent of the batteries fall?

5-18 One thousand inside diameters of a part were measured, and it was found that 23 measured less than 2.3425 in. and 159 measured more than 2.6425 in. Assuming normal distribution, determine the mean and the standard deviation of the measurements. How many parts would you expect to fall between 2.4425 and 2.7425 in.? How many would you expect to be larger than 2.8715 in.?

5-19 A series of 36 measurements of a manufactured part gave an arithmetic mean of 0.3420 in., with a standard error of the mean of 0.00187 in. A subsequent single measurement of 0.3063 in. was made by a junior engineer. Do you have any reason to question the validity of the junior engineer's measurement? Show proof.

5-20 The following data represent a statistical analysis of the repair times for a group of radar systems:

X, hr	f	v'	fv'	fv'^2
6.0	3	-2.0	-6.0	12.00
6.5	7	-1.5	-10.5	15.75
7.0	17	-1.0	-17.0	17.00
7.5	30	-0.5	-15.0	7.50
8.0	28	0	0	0.00
8.5	19	0.5	9.5	4.75
9.0	10	1.0	10.0	10.00
9.5	8	1.5	12.0	18.00
10.0	2	2.0	4.0	8.00

Find the mean repair time, the standard deviation, the median, the mode, and the limits within which 50 percent of the repair times would fall.

5-21 Refer to Prob. 4-10. What is the standard error of the mean? What is the 90 percent confidence limits on the average temperature?

5-22 From a known normally distributed sample a student made the calculations

$$R = 18 \qquad n = 36 \qquad \sigma_m = 1.5$$

Does the standard error of the mean appear reasonable? Explain.

5-23 A series of 25 repeated measurements of the thickness of a certain metallic block gave an arithmetic mean of 0.5871 in., with a standard error of the mean of 0.0005 in. If a subsequent single measurement were found to be 0.5785 in., would you have any reason to question its validity? Show proof.

5-24 The standard error of the mean for 25 measurements of a part is found to be 2.4 in. Find the standard deviation. What must be the total number of measurements if the standard error of the mean is to be reduced to 1.5 in.?

5-25 A steel fabricator has tested riveted joints and has found $\bar{X} = 3,210$ lb and $\sigma_s = 180$ lb for a sample of 100 joints. What is the 90 percent confidence interval for the average load carried by the joint? What is the minimum value you would expect at the 90 percent level if you were to test one more sample?

5-26 Refer to Prob. 4-11. Does it seem likely that the beams of different design are equivalent? Show your calculations. Is enough known to determine whether one beam is superior to the other? Why?

5-27 Traffic studies before and after a traffic-control device was installed resulted in the following data:

	$\overline{X}$, mph	σ_s	n
Before	18.2	3.51	140
After	19.2	3.15	160

Did the control device significantly affect the average speed on the street?

5-28 The average height of 121 male students selected at random from the student body of a large university was found to be 70.12 in., with a standard deviation of 2.75 in. What would be the 98 percent confidence limits for the average height of males at this university?

5-29 Two different brands of automobile tires were tested for the amount of wear after 20,000 miles of driving under the same conditions and rotation. The measure of wear was weight loss, expressed as a percentage of the initial weight:

	$\overline{X}$, %	σ_s	n
Brand A	15.0	1.2	144
Brand B	14.5	1.8	81

Can we conclude that brand B gives significantly more mileage than brand A?

5-30 Two companies produced the same new product; tests of both products gave the following data:

	$\overline{X}$	σ_s	n
Plant A	62	7.2	11
Plant B	69	8.4	14

Determine whether these two companies are making significantly different products.

5-31 Two manufacturing processes are to be compared. For the first process a sample of size 100 is found to have a mean of 107 and a standard deviation of 17. For the second process a sample size of 90 has a mean of 103 and a standard deviation of 16. Is there a significant difference between the means of the two processes?

5-32 The amount of tar in two different brands of cigarettes was determined by a testing laboratory, with the following results:

	$\bar{X}$, mg	σ_s	n
Brand A	11.52	0.25	100
Brand B	11.44	0.13	81

Would you say that there was a significant difference in the amount of tar in the two brands?

5-33 Two engineering classes independently measured the static coefficient of friction of brass on wood by a technique known to be free of systematic errors. Their results were as follows:

Class I		Class II	
X	f	X	f
0.40–0.42	2	0.42–0.44	4
0.42–0.44	10	0.44–0.46	16
0.44–0.46	18	0.46–0.48	20
0.46–0.48	16	0.48–0.50	17
0.48–0.50	9	0.50–0.52	3
0.50–0.52	5	0.52–0.54	4

On the basis of these data alone, is there a significant difference in the results of the two classes?

5-34 One hundred resistors of brand *X* were tested, and it was determined that 68.3 percent had a life of 285 to 315 hr, with a normal distribution. A manufacturer of brand *Y* resistors claimed his product had a longer life; subsequently 144 resistors of brand *Y* were tested and found to follow a normal distribution, with 50 percent having a life of 296.6 to 309.4 hr. Are the resistors of brand *Y* significantly better than those of brand *X*? Show proof.

5-35 The life of two types of electric light bulbs was tested, with the following results:

	$\bar{X}$, hr	σ_s	n
Brand A	1,360	80	100
Brand B	1,380	60	144

Does the life of these two types of bulbs differ significantly?

5-36   The gasoline mileage of 50 cars of make F had a mean of 19.1 miles/gal, with a standard deviation of 2.5 miles/gal, while that for 70 cars of make C had a mean of 20.0 miles/gal, with a standard deviation of 3.0 miles/gal. On the basis of these data, can we conclude that cars of make C consume significantly less gasoline than those of make F?

six

error
propagation

Exactel Instrument

We have seen how probability and statistics play an important role in the study of measurements and their underlying distributions. Now let us see what happens when we manipulate data subject to randomness. Many of our day-to-day calculations contain errors that fall into the category of randomness. The fact that our measuring process never provides us with the true mean of the population is one type of random error. It follows that when we use data containing random errors in mathematical calculations the errors are propagated by our calculations. Engineers and scientists are especially concerned about the magnitude of these propagated errors. In the space industry, for example, errors can reach such magnitudes as to cause systems to fail, and frequently the designer must be able to estimate errors in a system before the system is put in operation. Information about the individual figures that go into a calculation will provide him with some idea of the errors that might exist in the final results. Error propagation in digital computers, which may in some cases invalidate the entire calculation, has been the subject of much study.

As an illustration of the effect of the propagation of random errors consider a manufacturing process, in which a bearing is to be placed on a shaft. The workman randomly selects a bearing to place on a shaft which he has also randomly selected. There is certainly a probability that he may have selected a shaft which is larger than the exact specified value and a bearing whose diameter is smaller than the exact specified value. We should be able to predict the percentage of time such interference will occur or to design products so that it will rarely occur. Let us discuss some general topics before we return to this problem.

We saw in Chapter Four that the variation of a group of measurements is given by the variance. We need a similar parameter for results of various calculations. As a matter of fact, we use the same parameter. Appendix E shows the general forms for evaluating the variance of different fundamental calculations. In this chapter we will expand on these general forms in detail and give examples of each. As shown in Chapter Five, we usually employ $\sigma_m{}^2$ as the prediction parameter when we are dealing with prediction of mean values; thus the derivations in Appendix E are in terms of σ_m. This derivation would have been just as valid if σ_0 had been used. The important point is that we use the same parameter for each measure of variation and do not mix σ_m with σ_0 in the same calculation.

6-2 ERROR PROPAGATION IN ADDITION AND SUBTRACTION

In deriving an expression for the standard error of means we found that the variance was the sum of the individual variances. The general term for the variance for calculations involving only addition or subtraction is given by Eq. E-2,

$$\sigma_{m_\pm}^2 = \sigma_{m_1}^2 + \sigma_{m_2}^2 + \cdots + \sigma_{m_n}^2$$

We may write this in a slightly different form as

$$\sigma_{m_\pm} = \sqrt{\sigma_{m_1}^2 + \sigma_{m_2}^2 + \cdots + \sigma_{m_n}^2} \qquad \textbf{6-1}$$

where the secondary subscript $\pm$ indicates the operation involved.

For some level of confidence other than 68.3 percent, we simply multiply by the proper Z value (Z equals 1.0 in this case). Thus

$$Z\sigma_{m_\pm} = Z\sqrt{\sigma_{m_1}^2 + \sigma_{m_2}^2 + \cdots + \sigma_{m_n}^2}$$

or

$$Z\sigma_{0_\pm} = Z\sqrt{\sigma_{0_1}^2 + \sigma_{0_2}^2 + \cdots + \sigma_{0_n}^2}$$

example 6-1 In weighting soil samples with a balance scale the following weights were required to just balance the specimen:

No. of weights	Weights used, lb	σ_m, lb
1	3	0.01
1	$\frac{3}{4}$	0.004
1	$\frac{1}{10}$	0.002

Given the standard error for the weights, what are the 95 percent confidence limits on the actual weight of the sample?

The total weight is 3.85 lb $\pm$ error. The variance is

$$\sigma_m{}^2 = 0.01^2 + 0.004^2 + 0.002^2 = 0.00012$$

and the standard error is thus

$$\sigma_m = 0.00012^{\frac{1}{2}} = 0.01095$$

Hence the error at the 95 percent level is

$$Z\sigma_m = 2\sigma_m = 0.0219$$

and the weight is 3.85 $\pm$ 0.0219 lb.

This example is meant only as an illustration. In general the weights used in laboratories have such small standard errors that the results are rarely affected. This is one reason that such care is taken to keep the weights clean and damage free.

example 6-2   Two mating parts are being received from different manufacturers. In order to determine the 99 percent confidence limits on tolerance of fit the following samples were taken from the supply of parts:

	$\overline{X}$, in.	σ_s	n
Female	0.510	0.020	100
Male	0.495	0.021	50

What are the tolerance limits for the parts?

The tolerance range is the difference between male and female parts, $0.510 - 0.495 = 0.015$ in. Since the error is $Z\sigma_m$, where

$$Z = 2.326 \qquad \sigma_m = \left(\frac{0.020^2}{100} + \frac{0.021^2}{50}\right)^{\frac{1}{2}} = 0.0036$$

the tolerance is

$$0.015 \pm 2.326 \times 0.0036 = 0.015 \pm 0.0084$$
$$= 0.015 \pm 0.008 \text{ in.}$$

Thus at the 99 percent confidence level the maximum tolerance is 0.023 in. and the minimum tolerance is 0.007 in.

6-3 ERROR PROPAGATION IN MULTIPLICATION

We make many calculations involving products of numbers containing random errors. Probably the most frequent is the calculation of area and volume. The general form for products involving different measurements is given by Eq. E-3 as

$$\sigma_m^2 = \overline{X}_2^2 \sigma_{m_1}^2 + \overline{X}_1^2 \sigma_{m_2}^2$$

$$= \frac{\overline{X}_1^2 \overline{X}_2^2}{\overline{X}_1^2} \sigma_{m_1}^2 + \frac{\overline{X}_2^2 \overline{X}_1^2}{\overline{X}_2^2} \sigma_{m_2}^2$$

$$= \overline{X}_1^2 \overline{X}_2^2 \left(\frac{\sigma_{m_1}^2}{\overline{X}_1^2} + \frac{\sigma_{m_2}^2}{\overline{X}_2^2} \right)$$

or by Eq. E-4 as

$$\sigma_m^2 = \overline{X}_1^2 \overline{X}_2^2 \overline{X}_3^2 \overline{X}_4^2 \left(\frac{\sigma_{m_1}^2}{\overline{X}_1^2} + \frac{\sigma_{m_2}^2}{\overline{X}_2^2} + \frac{\sigma_{m_3}^2}{\overline{X}_3^2} + \frac{\sigma_{m_4}^2}{\overline{X}_4^2} \right)$$

(If the measurements are all equal see Sec. 6-5.) It is apparent that these two expressions are generally the same, the only difference being the number of terms involved. Let us now restate this relation as

$$\sigma_{m_\times} = \overline{X}_1 \overline{X}_2 \overline{X}_3 \cdots \overline{X}_n \left(\frac{\sigma_{m_1}^2}{\overline{X}_1^2} + \frac{\sigma_{m_2}^2}{\overline{X}_2^2} + \frac{\sigma_{m_3}^2}{\overline{X}_3^2} + \cdots + \frac{\sigma_{m_n}^2}{\overline{X}_n^2} \right)^{\frac{1}{2}}$$

6-2

where the secondary subscript $\times$ indicates a product.

example 6-3 A rectangular field was measured several times with the following results:

	$\overline{X}, ft$	σ_s	n
Width	250.7	0.5	25
Length	375.1	0.6	25

What is the standard error of the area?

Writing Eq. E-3 as

$$\sigma_{m_x}{}^2 = (\overline{X}_2 \sigma_{m_1})^2 + (\overline{X}_1 \sigma_{m_2})^2$$

we have

$$\sigma_{m_x} = [(\overline{X}_2 \sigma_{m_1})^2 + (\overline{X}_1 \sigma_{m_2})^2]^{\frac{1}{2}}$$

Since

$$\sigma_{m_1} = \frac{0.5}{\sqrt{25}} = 0.1 \quad \text{and} \quad \sigma_{m_2} = \frac{0.6}{\sqrt{25}} = 0.12$$

the standard error is

$$\sigma_{m_x} = [(375.1 \times 0.1)^2 + (250.7 \times 0.12)^2]^{\frac{1}{2}} = 49 \text{ ft}^2$$

6-4 ERROR PROPAGATION IN DIVISION

The expression for division by more than one term can be quite complicated, and so we will restrict ourselves to the case where we have only one term in both the numerator and the denominator (note that we can reduce a series of products in the numerator or denominator to a single term by means of Eq. 6-2). The general relation is given by Eq. E-5 as

$$\sigma_{m_{\div}}{}^2 = \frac{\overline{X}_1{}^2}{\overline{X}_2{}^2} \left(\frac{\sigma_{m_1}{}^2}{\overline{X}_1{}^2} + \frac{\sigma_{m_2}{}^2}{\overline{X}_2{}^2} \right)$$

or

$$\sigma_{m_{\div}} = \left[\frac{\overline{X}_1{}^2}{\overline{X}_2{}^2} \left(\frac{\sigma_{m_1}{}^2}{\overline{X}_1{}^2} + \frac{\sigma_{m_2}{}^2}{\overline{X}_2{}^2} \right) \right]^{\frac{1}{2}}$$

We may rewrite this as

$$\sigma_{m_{\div}} = \frac{\overline{X}_1}{\overline{X}_2} \sqrt{ \frac{\sigma_{m_1}{}^2}{\overline{X}_1{}^2} + \frac{\sigma_{m_2}{}^2}{\overline{X}_2{}^2} } \qquad \qquad \textbf{6-3}$$

where the secondary subscript $\div$ indicates the operation.

example 6-4 Find the error in the quotient of A/B if $A = 50.00$ ft^2, with $\sigma_{m_A} = 0.12$ ft^2, and $B = 10.00$ ft, with $\sigma_{m_B} = 0.09$ ft.

Using Eq. 6-3,

where

$$\overline{X}_1 = A = 50.00 \qquad \sigma_{m_1} = \sigma_{m_A} = 0.12$$

and

$$\overline{X}_2 = B = 10.00 \qquad \sigma_{m_2} = \sigma_{m_B} = 0.09$$

we have

$$\sigma_{m_\div} = \frac{\overline{X}_1}{\overline{X}_2} \sqrt{\frac{\sigma_{m_1}^2}{\overline{X}_1^2} + \frac{\sigma_{m_2}^2}{\overline{X}_2^2}}$$

$$= \frac{50.00}{10.00} \sqrt{\frac{0.12^2}{50.00^2} + \frac{0.09^2}{10.00^2}}$$

$$= 5 \sqrt{0.0000058 + 0.000081} = 5 \times 0.0093$$

$$= 0.0465 \text{ ft}$$

6-5 *ERROR PROPAGATION IN POWERS AND ROOTS*

In general the expressions for powers and roots are similar, except that in one case the exponent is fractional and in the other case it is a whole number. Equations E-6 and E-7 are modified to give σ_m and shown in Eqs. 6-4 and 6-5.

The expression for powers, given by Eq. E-6, is modified here as

$$\sigma_{m_{\text{power}}} = n\overline{X}^{n-1} \sigma_m \qquad\qquad \textbf{6-4}$$

and the expression for roots, given by Eq. E-7, is modified as

$$\sigma_{m_{\text{root}}} = \frac{\overline{X}^{1/n}}{n\overline{X}} \sigma_m \qquad\qquad \textbf{6-5}$$

example 6-5 A machine can produce each face of a cube with equal precision. If each face averages 2 in., with a standard error of 0.01 in., what is the standard error of the volume of the cube?

The volume is

$$\overline{X}^3 = 2^3 = 8 \text{ in.}^3$$

Hence the standard error is

$$\sigma_{m_{\text{power}}} = n\overline{X}^{n-1}\sigma_m = 3 \times 2^2 \times 0.01 = \pm 0.12 \text{ in.}^3$$

6-6 *GENERAL ERROR PROPAGATION*

There are many situations in which we must deal with combinations of the fundamental calculations. We may evaluate such expressions by using Eq. E-1 as shown in the last section of Appendix E or by algebra and the basic forms presented so far. Consider the following two examples of the use of algebra to develop the proper expression for the variance of combinations.

example 6-6 What is the correct expression for the standard error of a volume where two of the three sides have the same mean and standard error?

The volume $\overline{X}_1^2 \overline{X}_2$ is clearly a product of A and B, where $A = \overline{X}_1^2$ and $B = \overline{X}_2$. Hence

$$\sigma_{m_\times} = AB\sqrt{\left(\frac{\sigma_{m_A}}{A}\right)^2 + \left(\frac{\sigma_{m_B}}{B}\right)^2}$$

where

$$\sigma_{m_A} = n\overline{X}^{n-1}\sigma_{m_1} = 2\overline{X}_1\sigma_{m_1} \qquad \sigma_{m_B} = \sigma_{m_2}$$

Substituting for A and B, we have

$$\sigma_{m_\times} = \overline{X}_1{}^2 \overline{X}_2 \sqrt{\left(\frac{2\overline{X}_1 \sigma_{m_1}}{\overline{X}_1{}^2}\right)^2 + \left(\frac{\sigma_{m_2}}{\overline{X}_2}\right)^2}$$

$$= \overline{X}_1{}^2 \overline{X}_2 \sqrt{\left(\frac{2\sigma_{m_1}}{\overline{X}_1}\right)^2 + \left(\frac{\sigma_{m_2}}{\overline{X}_2}\right)^2}$$

This expression agrees directly with case 1 in Appendix E, which was solved by means of calculus and Eq. E-1.

example 6-7 Find the expression for the standard error of $C^2 \sqrt{D}$.

Once again we handle this as the product of A and B, where

$$A = C^2 = \overline{X}_1{}^2 \qquad B = D = \overline{X}_2$$

Since

$$\sigma_{m_\times} = \sqrt{(B\sigma_{m_A})^2 + (A\sigma_{m_B})^2}$$

where

$$\sigma_{m_A} = n\overline{X}_1{}^{n-1}\sigma_{m_1} = 2\overline{X}_1\sigma_{m_1} \qquad \sigma_{m_B} = \frac{\overline{X}_2{}^{1/n}}{n\overline{X}_2}\sigma_{m_2} = \frac{\sigma_{m_2}}{2\sqrt{\overline{X}_2}}$$

substitution yields

$$\sigma_{m_\times} = \sqrt{(\sqrt{\overline{X}_2}\,2\overline{X}_1\sigma_{m_1})^2 + \left(\frac{\overline{X}^2\sigma_{m_2}}{2\sqrt{\overline{X}_2}}\right)^2}$$

This is the same as case 2 in Appendix E.

6-7 CURVE FITTING

Let us now consider some aspects of data collection, which provides us, after all, with the information for our statistical treatment. In many instances we will want to predict the relationship between two observed variables. For example, we may want to know the relationship of shaft horsepower to revolutions per minute for an engine, or the way in which a capacitor charge changes with time. The observed data in such cases are rarely exactly consistent with some defining equation, and to determine the relationship we must fit a curve to the data and note its "goodness of fit."

In this section we will examine the theory of *least-squares curve fitting*. Part of the derivation is necessarily beyond the mathematical scope of this text, and the equations are presented here without proof. Once we have solved the problem of linear curve fitting, we can expand the theory to the general case for an *n*th-degree curve, which is solved by computer application. Finally, an equation is given for developing a confidence interval for the estimated values obtained from the fitted-curve equation.

linear least-squares curve fitting

When we use the least-squares method to solve for the curve describing our observed data we must determine which of the two variables is to be the *independent variable*. This is often the easier of the two variables to measure. In the example above, revolutions per minute, not horsepower, would probably be chosen as the independent variable. We then develop our equations so that we can predict the other variable, which becomes the *dependent variable*. In the equations for curve fitting we will chose x as the independent variable and y as the dependent variable. Reversing this notation yields different results for the equations of the line.

Figure 6-1 shows the relation used in developing equations for linear curve fitting, often called *linear regression*. The general form of a linear equation is

$$y = a + bx$$

We see from the figure that a represents the y intercept and b the slope of the line, and that we are estimating values of y from observed values of x; that is,

$$\hat{y}_i = a + bx_i$$

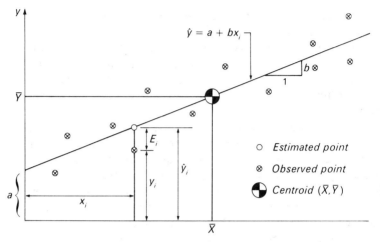

figure 6-1   Relationship of terms in linear regression equations

where $\hat{y}_i$ is the estimated value of the dependent variable y_i. The error E_i is given by

$$E_i = y_i - \hat{y}_i$$

The least-squares theorem states that we are to minimize the summation of the square of the errors,

$$E_{\min} = \sum_{i=1}^{n} (y_i - \hat{y}_i)^2 \quad \text{minimized}$$

In order to perform this minimization we use calculus, setting the derivative to zero. This process will generate two equations with two unknowns. Minimizing

$$\sum_{i=1}^{n} (y_i - \hat{y}_i)^2, \quad \text{where } \hat{y}_i = a + bx_i,$$

we obtain

$$\sum_{i=1}^{n} (y_i - a - bx_i)^2$$

Then, setting

$$\frac{\partial f}{\partial a} = 0 \qquad \frac{\partial f}{\partial b} = 0$$

we have

$$\frac{\partial f}{\partial a} = 0 = -2\Sigma(y_i - a - bx_i)$$

$$\frac{\partial f}{\partial b} = 0 = -2\Sigma x_i(y_i - a - bx_i)$$

which yield

$$\sum_{i=1}^{n} (y_i - a - bx_i) = 0 \qquad\qquad \textbf{6-6}$$

and

$$\sum_{i=1}^{n} (y_i x_i - ax_i - bx_i^2) = 0 \qquad\qquad \textbf{6-7}$$

The derivation may now be followed without calculus from these two general equations. If we reduce Eq. 6-6 to obtain

$$\Sigma y_i - \Sigma a - b\Sigma x_i = 0$$

and then multiply both sides by $1/n$,

$$\frac{\Sigma y_i}{n} - \frac{na}{n} - \frac{b\Sigma x_i}{n} = 0$$

our final result is

$$\overline{Y} = a + b\overline{X} \qquad\qquad \textbf{6-8}$$

Equation 6-8 implies that the curve will pass through the centroid $(\overline{X}, \overline{Y})$, which can also be seen from Fig. 6-1. Rewriting Eq. 6-8 yields

$$a = \overline{Y} - b\overline{X} \qquad\qquad \textbf{6-9}$$

Next we reduce Eq. 6-7,

$$\Sigma x_i y_i - a\Sigma x_i - b\Sigma x_i^2 = 0$$

and multiply the second term by n/n,

$$\Sigma x_i y_i - an\overline{X} - b\Sigma x_i^2$$

Then substituting Eq. 6-9 for a, we have

$$\Sigma x_i y_i - (\overline{Y} - b\overline{X}) n\overline{X} - b\Sigma x_i^2$$

which may be rearranged as

$$b\Sigma x_i^2 = \Sigma x_i y_i - n\overline{Y}\,\overline{X} + bn\overline{X}^2$$

or

$$b(\Sigma x_i^2 - n\overline{X}^2) = \Sigma x_i y_i - n\overline{Y}\,\overline{X}$$

Hence

$$b = \frac{\Sigma x_i y_i - n\overline{Y}\,\overline{X}}{\Sigma x_i^2 - n\overline{X}^2} \qquad\qquad \textbf{\textit{6-10}}$$

We may use Eq. 6-10 to evaluate b and then substitute this value into Eq. 6-9 to find a; this then gives the estimating equation $\hat{y}_i = a + bx_i$. Equation 6-10 can be converted into a more convenient form for use with a desk calculator by multiplying the right-hand side by n/n. This form is shown in Table 6-1, which gives convenient forms for evaluation by calculator or by hand. A simple example will show the application of these equations in hand calculation.

table 6-1   *Linear least-squares equations (linear regression)*

	Variable	Equations
Calculator	b	$b = \dfrac{n\Sigma x_i y_i - \Sigma x_i \Sigma y_i}{n\Sigma x_i^2 - (\Sigma x_i)^2}$
	a	$a = \dfrac{\Sigma y_i}{n} - \dfrac{b\Sigma x_i}{n}$
Hand calculation using grouped data (see Chapter Four)		$\bar{v}_x = \dfrac{\Sigma v_{x_j}}{n} \qquad \bar{v}_y = \dfrac{\Sigma v_{y_j}}{n}$
		$\overline{X} = I_x \bar{v}_x + \bar{x}' \qquad \overline{Y} = I_y \bar{v}_y + \overline{Y}'$
	b	$b = \dfrac{(\Sigma v_{x_j} v_{y_j}/n - \bar{v}_x \bar{v}_y) I_x I_y}{I_x^2(\Sigma v_{x_i}^2/n - \bar{v}_x^2)}$
	a	$a = \overline{Y} - b\overline{X}$

example 6-8   Given the following data, use least squares to find a linear equation that best fits the data:

x	1	2	3	4	5	6	7	8	9	10
y	5	8	8	9	10	10	10	12	13	13

To simplify the evaluation let us use a tabular form similar to those in Chapter Four. From the table below,

f_j	x_j	y_j	v_{x_j}	v_{y_j}	$v_x v_y$	$v_x{}^2$	$v_y{}^2$
1	1	5	-4	-5	20	16	25
1	2	8	-3	-2	6	9	4
1	3	8	-2	-2	4	4	4
1	4	9	-1	-1	1	1	1
1	5	10	0	0	0	0	0
1	6	10	1	0	0	1	0
1	7	10	2	0	0	4	0
1	8	10	3	2	6	9	4
1	9	13	4	3	12	16	9
1	10	13	5	3	15	25	9

$$\Sigma v_{x_j} = 5 \qquad \Sigma v_{y_j} = -2 \qquad \Sigma v_x v_y = 64 \qquad \Sigma v_x{}^2 = 85$$

$$\Sigma v_y{}^2 = 56$$

Now, since

$$I_x = 1 \qquad I_y = 1 \qquad \overline{X}' = 5 \qquad \overline{Y}' = 10$$

we have

$$\bar{v}_x = \frac{\Sigma v_{x_j}}{n} = \frac{5}{10} = 0.5 \qquad \bar{v}_y = \frac{\Sigma v_{x_j}}{n} = \frac{-2}{10} = -0.2$$

$$\overline{X} = I_x \bar{v}_x + \overline{X}' = 1 \times 0.5 + 5 = 5.5$$

$$\overline{Y} = I_y \bar{v}_y + \overline{Y}' = 1 \times 0.2 + 10 = 9.8$$

Then

$$b = \frac{(\Sigma v_{x_j} v_{y_j}/n - \bar{v}_x \bar{v}_y) I_x I_y}{I_x{}^2 (\Sigma v_{x_i}{}^2/n - \bar{v}_x{}^2)} = \frac{(\frac{64}{10} - 0.1) 1 \times 1}{1^2 (\frac{85}{10} - 0.25^2)} = \frac{6.5}{8.25}$$

$$= 0.79$$

and

$$a = \bar{Y} - b\bar{X} = 9.8 - 0.79 \times 5.5 = 4.47$$

Hence

$$\hat{y} = 4.47 + 0.79x$$

equations of second degree and higher

Suppose our data are not linear. We fit a curve in the same way, expanding the estimating equation to order n. Let us first consider the expansion to a second-degree equation and from that proceed to the general equation for the nth-degree regression.

We let $\hat{y}$ have the second-degree form

$$\hat{y} = a + bx + cx^2 \qquad \qquad \textbf{6-11}$$

Then, setting

$$\frac{\partial f}{\partial a} = 0 \qquad \frac{\partial f}{\partial b} = 0 \qquad \frac{\partial f}{\partial c} = 0$$

we have

$$\Sigma(y_i - a - bx_i - cx_i^2) = 0 \qquad \qquad \textbf{6-12}$$

$$\Sigma x_i(y_i - a - bx_i - cx_i^2) = 0 \qquad \qquad \textbf{6-13}$$

$$\Sigma x_i^2(y_i - a - bx_i - cx_i^2) = 0 \qquad \qquad \textbf{6-14}$$

We may now use calculus to expand Eqs. 6-12 to 6-14 and regroup them as

$$\Sigma y_i = an + b\Sigma x_i + c\Sigma x_i^2$$

$$\Sigma y_i x_i = a\Sigma x_i + b\Sigma x_i^2 + c\Sigma x_i^3$$

$$\Sigma y_i x_i^2 = a\Sigma x_i^2 + b\Sigma x_i^3 + c\Sigma x_i^4$$

We then solve these three equations simultaneously to find values for a, b, and c.

In this form the equations can be expanded into a general set of equations for an nth-degree curve:

$$\Sigma y_i x_i^0 = a_1 \Sigma x_i^0 + a_2 \Sigma x_i^1 + \cdots + a_{n+1} \Sigma x_i^n$$
$$\Sigma y_i x_i^1 = a_1 \Sigma x_i^1 + a_2 \Sigma x_i^2 + \cdots + a_{n+1} \Sigma x_i^{n+1}$$
$$\cdots\cdots\cdots\cdots\cdots\cdots\cdots\cdots\cdots\cdots\cdots\cdots\cdots\cdots\cdots\cdots$$
$$\Sigma y_i x_i^n = a_1 \Sigma x_i^n + a_2 \Sigma x_i^{n+1} + \cdots + a_{n+1} \Sigma x_i^{2n}$$

These equations are readily solved on a digital computer; however, some errors result from the great difference in magnitude of numbers, and care must be taken in evaluating the results. This error is magnified with increasing order of regression, as the last term in the last simultaneous equation is always a summation of x_i^{2n}.

goodness of fit

The estimating equation obtained from the least-squares method does not predict exactly the values obtained from observation. This is because of randomness of the dependent variable; if we were to hold a single value of the independent variable constant, we would obtain data similar to those in Fig. 6-2. This is the same distribution we studied in earlier chapters, and $\hat{y}$ could be considered the mean of possible values of y at a given value of x. Therefore it

figure 6-2   *Random variation of y at a given value of x*

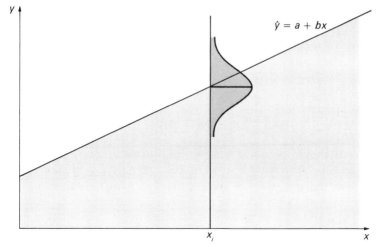

should be possible to evaluate a standard deviation for y at the given value of x. In the study of curve fitting it is sometimes assumed that there is a normal-distribution function the length of the estimating curve, as shown in Fig. 6-3. This entire distribution of y values along the regression line is then assumed to have a constant standard deviation given by

$$\sigma_{y \text{ on } x} \simeq \sigma_{s \, y \text{ on } x} = \left\{ \frac{n}{n-2} \left[\sigma_y^2 - \frac{(\Sigma x_i y_i / n - \overline{X}\,\overline{Y})^2}{\sigma_x^2} \right] \right\}^{\frac{1}{2}}$$

$$6\text{-}15$$

where

$$\sigma_y^2 = \frac{\sum\limits_{i=1}^{n} (y_i - \overline{Y})^2}{n} = \frac{\sum\limits_{i=1}^{n} y_i^2}{n} - \overline{Y}^2$$

and

$$\sigma_x^2 = \frac{\sum\limits_{i=1}^{n} x_i^2}{n} - \overline{X}^2$$

(For the development see advanced texts on statistics.) This standard deviation is called the *standard deviation of y on x*.

The final form of the estimating equation,

$$\hat{y} = a + bx \pm Z\sigma_{y \text{ on } x} \qquad \text{with a given confidence level} \quad 6\text{-}16$$

is readily developed from previous calculations for the regression equation.

It should be noted that not all data are evenly distributed around the regression line, as was assumed in this section. Even distribution was assumed here to indicate that the results of the regression equation are only approximate. The problems of regression and goodness of fit are discussed in greater detail in advanced texts on the subject.

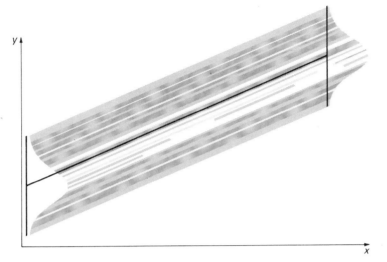

figure 6-3   Uniform distribution of y values around regression line
$y = a + bx$

SUMMARY

Errors in measurements which are themselves mean values of a distribution are propagated in subsequent mathematical calculations. Hence the uncertainty in the results of basic arithmetic and algebra operations is greater than the uncertainty in any individual term. The magnitude of this uncertainty is a function of the particular operation.

The relationship between two variables is analyzed by the least-squares method to establish, or in certain cases predict, the underlying functional equation. This process provides an expression which best fits the observed data. An expression similar to the standard deviation of a single variable expresses the goodness of fit.

PROBLEMS

6-1 Given the following measurements in feet, find the sum and its error.

261.35 ± 0.005
14.31 ± 0.002
132.43 ± 0.003

6-2   If angle $A = 75°42'16'' \pm 4''$ and angle $B = 39°58'37'' \pm 3''$, find their difference and its error.

6-3   A rectangular lot is 50.00 ± 0.01 ft by 100.00 ± 0.02 ft. Compute the error of the area.

6-4   Find the error in the volume of a cube that is 6.00 ± 0.03 in.

6-5   Find the error involved in obtaining the square root of 25.00 ± 0.005.

6-6   A rectangular area whose measurements are 10.00 ± 0.05 ft by 30.00 ± 0.09 ft is to be laid out. Compute the area and its error.

6-7   A rectangular area for a jig assembly has one fixed dimension AB of 15.00 ± 0.015 ft. If the area $ABCD$ is to be 300.00 ± 0.27 ft^2, what must be the dimension for the side AC or DB?

6-8   The radius r of a cylinder is given as 11.0 ± 0.2 cm and the height l as 12.3 ± 0.3 cm. Find its volume and the error.

6-9   If $P = 1.16 \pm 0.08$ in. and $Q = 2.54 \pm 0.12$ in., find the propagated error in the following operations:

  a $P + Q$
  b PQ
  c P^2

6-10   The volume of a sphere is given by the formula $V = \frac{4}{3}\pi r^3$, where r is the radius. If the radius of a sphere is measured and found to be 3.00 ± 0.04 cm, compute the volume and its error.

6-11   The volume of a sphere is $V = \frac{4}{3}\pi r^3$. If the radius of a sphere was measured and found to be 4.00 ± 0.02 in., compute the volume and its error.

6-12   The surface area of a right circular cylinder is given by the formula $S = 2\pi rh$. Find the surface area and its error if r was measured as 5.00 ± 0.08 cm and h as 7.00 ± 0.03 cm.

6-13 The volume of a sphere is computed from the equation $V = \pi d^3/6$. What is the uncertainty in this computed value if d is measured and found to be 5.00 ± 0.08 in.?

6-14 If measurements revealed $R = 2.000 \pm 0.0224$ in. and $T = 1.500 \pm 0.060$ in., compute the error in $4.3\ R^4 T$.

6-15 The period of a simple pendulum is given by

$$p = 2\pi \sqrt{\frac{1}{g}}$$

where p = period

l = length

g = acceleration due to gravity

If $l = 6.44 \pm 0.02$ ft and $g = 32.2 \pm 0.03$ ft/sec², find the probable error in p.

6-16 It is thought that the relationship between a spillway's velocity and corresponding water elevation is linear. Ten samples were taken, with the results

$\Sigma x_i^2 = 3291.2 \qquad \Sigma y^2 = 10272.1$

$\Sigma x_i y_i = 4372.1 \qquad \Sigma x_i = 152 \qquad \Sigma y_i = 203$

What straight-line equation would best fit these results? What are the 90 percent confidence limits on $\hat{y}$? Sketch the results showing a band on either side of the regression line at the 90 percent level.

6-17 In an experiment designed to test the horsepower output of an engine one of the things being observed with respect to horsepower was the speed of the shaft between the engine and the dynamic brake. The following data were obtained:

Horsepower	80	125	155	171	190	205	228	244
Shaft rpm	500 (idle)	1,000	1,500	2,000	2,500	3,000	3,500	4,000

Assuming that the data represent a linear relationship, solve for the values of a and b in the equation

$$\text{Horsepower} = a + b \,(\text{rpm})$$

Does the value of a appear reasonable? If not, can you explain what would be reasonable? Find the 95 percent confidence limits for horsepower when the shaft reading is 3,000 rpm. What do you predict the horsepower will be at 4,200 rpm?

6-18 An engineer is observing the drag on a body being pulled through a certain fluid and makes the following scaled measurements:

Drag	3	6	11	18	27
Velocity	1	2	3	4	5

A plot of the data shows that the drag increases rapidly with respect to velocity. It is noted at relatively low velocities that the drag is nearly equal to 2. Thus an assumption is made that $K = 2$. The engineer expects a relationship of the general form

$$D = K + v^n$$

where D = drag

$\quad\quad K$ = constant

$\quad\quad v$ = velocity

exp n is a power factor indicating the rate of increase in drag in respect to an increase in velocity

He sets up the relationship

$$\log(D - K) = n \log v$$

noting that this resembles

$$y = a + bx$$

where $y = \log(D - K)$ $a = 0$ $x = \log v$ $b = n$

and decides to solve for n by linear regression. What value of n does he find?

6-19 An examination is given to entering engineering freshmen which predicts the grade point they will achieve in engineering.

After the first year a random sample of students resulted in the following data:

Predicted grade	2.5 2.7 2.9 2.4 3.8 2.7 3.2 3.4 3.0 2.4 4.0 3.6 3.5 2.9 3.3
Actual	2.1 2.8 2.5 2.3 3.7 1.9 3.5 2.8 3.1 2.3 3.7 3.0 3.7 2.5 3.5

What would you predict as the value of a and b if the test were a very accurate predictor of expected grade point? Calculate the values of a and b. What is the significance of the calculated value of b? A friend hears that you have completed this study and asks you what range he can expect for his first year's grade point when the test predicts a 3.1. What would you tell him?

seven

dimensions
and unit systems

Boeing

In the preceding six chapters we have been concerned primarily with the numerical aspects of measurements. Only brief mention was made of the other, equally important characteristic of the measurement, its units. Engineers and scientists who make and use measurements recognize that in any statement about a physical variable units are just as important a part of the measurement as magnitude. A measurement expressed only in terms of its magnitude is virtually meaningless. In this chapter we will take a closer look at the dimensions and units we assign to physical variables and learn how to make important deductions about the relations which hold between the measured quantities associated with various physical phenomena. Familiarity with dimensions and units will eventually result in some sort of technique for handling them. However, the technique we now introduce is a concise and systematic method of dimensioning which can become a powerful tool for the engineer.

In general usage the dimensions of an object are its physical size and shape. In addition, the term *dimension* is used to designate the character of the physical quantity. For example, anything that can be measured in length units has the dimensions of length. It follows, then, that area has the dimensions of length squared and volume has the dimensions of length cubed. Here we are concerned only with the nature of the quantity, and not with its numerical measure or with any particular units, such as inches or feet. A dimension may be described as a generalized unit. The dimensions of most physical quantities are self-evident from their basic definitions, but as we will see later, occasionally they must be inferred from a physical law.

Dimensional nomenclature is by no means consistent. Generally capital letters are used to denote dimensions, such as L for length, F for force, T for time, and M for mass. In addition, square brackets are frequently used to denote the dimensions of the enclosed variable. Consider the meaning of the following dimensional equations:

$$[d] = L \qquad d \text{ has the dimension of length}$$
$$[p] = F \qquad p \text{ has the dimension of force}$$
$$[m] = M \qquad m \text{ has the dimension of mass}$$
$$[t] = T \qquad t \text{ has the dimension of time}$$

We will adhere to this notation in this text

7-2 DIMENSIONS AND DIMENSIONLESS QUANTITIES

fundamental dimensions

Space, time, and matter form the basis of our physical existence. Thus it should not be surprising that length, time, and mass are the basic dimensions representing these concepts. As a matter of fact, in mechanics all the quantities with which we are concerned can be expressed in terms of mass, length, and time. However, for reasons that have never been fully explained, engineers have adopted force as a basic concept instead of mass. We do not need to employ both mass and force as dimensions; their relationship is expressed by *Newton's second law* as $F \propto ma$. In the field of engineering the *fundamental dimensions* are usually *force F, length L*, and *time T*. Hence this force-based system is known as the *FLT system*. Physicists generally use a mass-based system, with *mass M, length L*, and *time T* as the fundamental dimensions. This system is known as the *MLT* or *absolute system*.

derived dimensions

When we combine fundamental dimensions, the resulting *derived dimensions* are usually determined by the definition of the quantity or by physical laws. For example, area has the derived dimensions of length squared (L^2) and volume has the derived dimensions of length cubed (L^3). Some additional secondary or derived dimensions commonly used by engineers are

$$\text{Pressure} = [p] = \frac{F}{L^2}$$

$$\text{Velocity} = [v] = \frac{L}{T}$$

$$\text{Acceleration} = [a] = \frac{L}{T^2}$$

$$\text{Work} = [u] = FL$$

$$\text{Power} = [P] = \frac{FL}{T}$$

Actually the distinction between fundamental and derived dimensions is an arbitrary one based principally on our perception of physical reality. If volume V had been selected as a fundamental dimension, for instance, then length would have the derived dimension of $V^{\frac{1}{3}}$. However, since we are more easily able to perceive length, it is length rather than volume that has been selected as fundamental.

dimensionless quantities

Some quantities have no units and are called *dimensionless* or *nondimensional quantities*, or *sterile values*. Examples are ratios, trigonometric functions, the number pi (π), the base of natural logarithms e, coefficients of friction, and specific gravity, all of which are expressed as pure numbers. Sometimes we say these quantities possess *null dimensions*. The capital letter N is used to indicate a dimensionless quantity:

$$[q] = N \qquad q \text{ has null dimensions or is a sterile value}$$

There are numerous dimensionless coefficients that have extensive applications in engineering calculations. Many of these are named for the person who introduced the term. For example,

$$[\text{Mach number}] = \frac{\text{representative velocity}}{\text{local speed of sound}} = \frac{L/T}{L/T} = N$$

$$[\text{Reynolds number}]$$

$$= \frac{\text{representative length} \times \text{representative velocity}}{\text{viscosity/density}}$$

$$= \frac{lv}{\mu/\rho} = \frac{\rho lv}{\mu} = \frac{M}{L^3} \frac{L}{T} L \frac{LT}{M}$$

$$= N \qquad \text{(the ratio of inertial to viscous forces)}$$

$$[\text{Knudsen number}] = \frac{\text{mean free path of molecules}}{\text{representative length}} = \frac{\lambda}{l}$$

$$= \frac{L}{L} = N \qquad \text{(flow patterns in rarefied gas dynamics)}$$

7-3 LAW OF DIMENSIONAL HOMOGENEITY

The *law of dimensional homogeneity* states that the expression or equation must be balanced dimensionally as well as numerically and must be valid whatever the system of units used. This means that the dimensions of all the sums in the equation must be the same and the dimensions of the left-hand side and the right-hand side must be the same. The dimensions as well as the values of physical quantities can be manipulated algebraically.

example 7-1 Determine if the following equation of uniformly accelerated motion is dimensionally homogeneous:

$$s = v_0 t + \tfrac{1}{2} a t^2$$

where s = displacement

$\qquad v_0$ = velocity

$\qquad a$ = acceleration

$\qquad t$ = time

We define

$$[s] = L \qquad [v_0] = \frac{L}{T} \qquad [a] = \frac{L}{T^2} \qquad [t] = T$$

Then, writing the equation dimensionally, we have

$$L = \frac{L}{T} T + \frac{L}{T^2} T^2$$

Note that the numerical coefficient is omitted from the dimensional analysis. Cancelling the dimensions algebraically, we find that $L = L + L$. Since we are not concerned with the numerical results, we find that the sum of two lengths is still just a length, so that $L = L$. This is proof that the dimensional character of the original expression is correct, and we would say that it is dimensionally homogeneous.

The law of dimensional homogeneity can also be used to ascertain information about specific terms making up the dimensional equation.

example 7-2 Determine the value of exp n in the dimensionally correct equation

$$by = Kd^n \frac{PR}{vy}$$

where b = volume per unit of time

$\quad d, y$ = lengths

$\quad\quad P$ = force per unit area

$\quad\quad v$ = viscosity with dimensions FT/L^2

$\quad K, R$ = sterile values

We define

$$[b] = \frac{L^3}{T} \qquad [K] = N \qquad [d] = L \qquad [P] = \frac{F}{L^2}$$

$$[R] = N \qquad [v] = \frac{FT}{L^2} \qquad [y] = L$$

Rewriting the equation in terms of dimensions only, we have

$$\frac{L^3}{T} L = NL^n \frac{(F/L^2)N}{(FT/L^2)L} = L^n \left(\frac{F}{L^2} \right) \left(\frac{L^2}{FT} \right) \frac{1}{L} = \frac{L^n}{LT}$$

or

$$L^n = L^4 L = L^5$$

Hence

$$\exp n = 5$$

example 7-3   Consider the dimensionally homogeneous expression

$$\frac{pv^2}{a} K = (B \tan \theta + B\pi - \tfrac{5}{3} l)\left(pl + \frac{pv^2}{2g} \cos 2\theta \right)$$

where v = velocity

a = area

l = length

p = force

g = acceleration

What are the dimensions of K and B?

Expressing the dimensions as

$$[v] = \frac{L}{T} \qquad [a] = L^2 \qquad [l] = L \qquad [p] = F$$

$$[g] = \frac{L}{T^2}$$

we may then rewrite the equation in terms of dimensions only as

$$\frac{FL^2/T^2}{L^2} [K] = (B + B - L)\left(FL + \frac{FL^2/T^2}{L/T^2} \right)$$

This cumbersome expression can be simplified by close inspection of the terms inside the first set of parentheses on the right-hand side. The expression $(B + B - L)$ gives us the information we need to determine the dimensions of B. Because of dimensional homogeneity, we can conclude that the only possible dimensions for B are those that will add or subtract with the dimension L; hence $[B] = L$. With this knowledge and some additional algebraic manipulations we can simplify the equation still further. Thus

$$\frac{F}{T^2}[K] = LFL$$

and so

$$[K] = \frac{LFLT^2}{F} = T^2 L^2$$

Here $T^2 L^2$ has no physical significance.

7-4 *INTRODUCTION TO DIMENSIONAL ANALYSIS*

Algebraic manipulation of the dimensions of physical quantities provides us with a great deal of information about the physical phenomena so described. The process by which we derive information about the mathematical form of a physical relation by an investigation of the dimensions is called *dimensional analysis*. We have already seen how this method may be used to check the correctness of a dimensional equation by ensuring that all the terms have the same dimensions. Another important use of dimensional analysis is testing scale models by comparison of the scale model with the original specifications. This particular phase of dimensional analysis has played a prominent role in engineering, particularly in the fields of aeronautics, hydraulics, heat transfer, and electromagnetics. Edgar Buckingham, a British mathematician, was largely responsible for providing a general expression for dimensional analysis, known as the *Buckingham π theorem*. A detailed discussion of all the aspects of dimensional analysis is beyond our scope, so let us now turn our attention to the units in which dimensions are expressed.

7-5 STANDARDS OF MEASUREMENT

Throughout recent history man has sought to establish measurement standards that can be reproduced with very high accuracy. In fact he has continually strived to improve the standards of measurement of the fundamental dimensions. Early attempts were quite crude; for example, the first adopted standard for a

table 7-1   Standards of measurements

Dimension	Unit	Definition
Length	Meter	*1791*: One-ten-millionth of the equator-to-pole distance on a meridian passing through Barcelona and Dunkirk *1889*: Distance between two engraved lines on a platinum-iridium international meter bar kept at Sevres, France *1960*: 1,650,763.73 wavelengths in a vacuum of the radiation emitted by the transition between two energy levels of krypton 86
Mass	Kilograms	*1791*: Mass of 1,000 cm^3 of water at 4° Celsius *1889*: Mass of the International Prototype Kilogram (a particular cylinder of platinum iridium) at Sevres, France
Time	Second	*1791*: 1/86,400 of a mean solar day *1967*: 9,192,631,770 cycles of the frequency associated with the transition between two energy levels of cesium 133
Temperature	Degree Celsius or Kelvin	*1791*: 1/100 of the interval between the freezing point of water (0° Celsius) and the boiling point of water (100° Celsius)* *1954*: 1/273.16 of the thermodynamic temperature of the triple point of water†

*The centigrade scale has been replaced by the Celsius scale.
†The triple point of water is the temperature at which the solid, liquid, and vapor phases of water exist together at equilibrium.

unit of length was part of the human body, a hand or foot. Nevertheless, most of these early standards sufficed until fairly recently, when it became necessary to control the accuracy of thousands of individual parts and components by reference to extremely accurate measurement standards.

In present-day technology there are many systems of units to describe measurements of the physical variables. Fortunately, all the fundamental dimensions except force and/or mass submit to a definition in terms of natural constants; force and mass have not yet been defined in such terms. The measurement standards as adopted by the General Conference on Weights and Measures are shown in Table 7-1, along with earlier definitions of historical interest.

7-6 UNIT SYSTEMS

Nearly all measurements are expressed in units. A *unit* may be defined as a selected magnitude of a physical variable which serves as a basis for comparison and in which other magnitudes of the same variable may be described. Thus a measurement of 15 ft has dimensions of length, where the unit of length is feet and the number 15 indicates how many times the unit must be duplicated to match the magnitude of the variable. The units that express the relationship of any system comprise a *unit system*.

It is frequently confusing to find two different unit systems used to describe the same physical variable. This problem is further compounded in the United States by the fact that most units used to describe the same quantity are not derivable from one another by a simple shift of the decimal point. At this point we will examine some of the unit systems in current use in science and engineering.

the meter-kilogram-second (mks) system

The mks system is a metric system based on absolute dimensions of mass, length, and time. At present over 90 percent of the world's population uses the metric system. This system is based on the dimensions and units shown in Table 7-2. Since mass, length, and time are fundamental dimensions, it is necessary to derive a

Dimension	Unit	Abbreviation
Mass M	Kilogram	kg
Length L	Meter	m
Time T	Second	sec

table 7-2

dimension for force by the relationship provided by Newton's second law,

$$F = ma$$

where $[m] = M$ $[a] = \dfrac{L}{T^2}$

Hence

$$[F] = \frac{ML}{T^2}$$

By substituting the appropriate units for mass and acceleration we get the unit of force called the *newton*, defined by

Newton $= \text{kg-m/sec}^2$

Hence one newton is the force required to give a mass of one kilogram an acceleration of one meter per second per second.

example 7-4   Solve for the mass in kilograms that is being accelerated at 4.79 m/sec² by a force of 8.72 newtons.

From Newton's law,

$$F = ma$$

or

$$m = \frac{F}{a} = \frac{8.72 \text{ kg-m/sec}^2}{4.79 \text{ m/sec}^2} = 1.82 \text{ kg}$$

centimeter-gram-second (cgs) system

The cgs system can be regarded as a practical modification of the mks system; hence it carries the connotation of being both

Dimension	Unit	Abbreviation
Mass M	Gram	gm
Length L	Centimeter	cm
Time T	Second	sec

table 7-3

metric and absolute. The cgs system is based on the dimensions and units shown in Table 7-3. Again we must derive dimensions and units for force, as follows:

$$F = ma$$

where $[m] = M \qquad [a] = \dfrac{L}{T^2}$

Thus

$$[F] = \frac{ML}{T^2}$$

By substitution we have the unit of force called the *dyne*, defined by

$$Dyne = g\text{-}cm/sec^2$$

That is, one dyne is the force required to give one gram of mass an acceleration of one centimeter per second per second.

example 7-5   Determine the force in dynes necessary to give 15.5 g of mass an acceleration of 3.52 cm/sec^2.

From the relation

$$F = ma$$

we have

$$F = 15.5 \text{ g} \times 3.52 \text{ cm/sec}^2 = 54.4 \text{ g-cm/sec}^2 = 54.4 \text{ dynes}$$

The British foot-pound-second (fps) system

The British fps system is a non metric absolute system based on the British units for mass, length, and time. Unfortunately, this system is sometimes given the abbreviation FPS; in such cases the capital F should not be confused with the fundamental dimension F for force.

The fundamental dimensions and units for the British fps system are shown in Table 7-4. The unit for force is derived as

$$F = ma$$

where

$$[m] = M \qquad [a] = \frac{L}{T^2}$$

Thus

$$[F] = \frac{ML}{T^2}$$

The unit of force is called the *poundal*, defined by

$$\text{Poundal} = \text{lb}_m\text{-ft/sec}^2$$

That is, one poundal is the force required to give one pound of mass an acceleration of one foot per second per second.

The term *poundal* is an unfortunate choice for the unit of force, since the unit of mass is the pound. It is seldom used by engineers.

example 7-6   What acceleration would result when a force of 15.5 poundals acts on a mass of 31.0 lb_m?

$$F = ma \qquad \text{or} \qquad a = \frac{F}{m}$$

Hence

$$a = \frac{15.5 \ \text{lb}_m\text{-ft/sec}^2}{31.0 \ \text{lb}_m} = 0.5 \ \text{ft/sec}^2$$

table 7-4

Dimension	Unit	Abbreviation
Mass M	Pound mass	lb_m
Length L	Foot	ft
Time T	Second	sec

the engineering foot-pound-second (fps) system

The engineering fps system, a gravitational system based on the dimensions force, length, and time, is in common use in the United States. Although the concept of the force seems very simple, it is by no means clearly defined. In spite of this engineers usually find it more convenient to work with forces rather than masses. The concept of force, which probably originated in cognizance of the muscular effort required to push or pull an object, prevailed until Newton made a clear distinction between weight and mass. There are many types of force—gravitational, electrostatic, magnetic, frictional, molecular. However, force is usually defined as an action exerted on a body which changes or tends to change its state of rest or uniform motion in a straight line. The force of gravity is characterized by its universality and the fact that its quantitative nature may be determined experimentally, but its actual nature is unknown.

In early engineering work the pound was used as a unit for both force and mass. For this reason pound force, abbreviated lb_f, denotes force and pound mass, lb_m, denotes mass. This distinction is frequently disregarded because in most engineering work pound force and pound mass are numerically equal. There are cases, however, where their values may differ widely. This is especially true at the extreme altitudes now reached by spacecraft.

To continue, *Newton's law of gravitation* states that there is an attraction between bodies such that

$$F = G \frac{m_1 m_2}{r^2}$$

where F = force of attraction

G = universal gravitational constant

m = mass

r = distance between the objects

The attractive force becomes appreciable when one mass is large, as is the case with the earth and objects on its surface. We call this force of attraction the *weight force* or simply the *weight* of the object.

As with other forces, its relation to mass and acceleration is given by Newton's second law,

$$F = ma$$

except that we now express it in different symbolics as

$$W = mg$$

where W = weight force

m = mass

g = acceleration due to the earth's gravity, which at sea level is approximately 32.2 ft/sec^2

Note that weight is a function of mass and the acceleration due to gravity.

Consider an object on the surface of the earth, as shown in Fig. 7-1. As an idealization we will consider each body as a particle, with its entire mass concentrated at the center of gravity. Here the weight force $W = m_2 g$ is the force of attraction between the earth and the object, which can be computed from

$$F = G \frac{m_1 m_2}{r^2}$$

where $F = W$. Therefore

$$m_2 g = G \frac{m_1 m_2}{r^2}$$

from which it is apparent that the mass of the object m_2 cancels, and that the mass of the earth m_1 is a constant and G is a constant; hence

$$g \propto \frac{1}{r^2}$$

This indicates that g varies inversely as the square of the distance between the objects. Thus if we were to move the same object to a different elevation, say to the top of Mt. Everest, as shown in Fig. 7-2, g would be less because of the increase in the distance r. Since

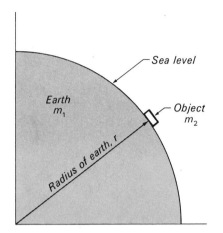

figure 7-1   Weight force
of an object
on earth's surface

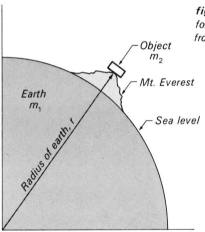

figure 7-2   Change in weight
force with distance
from earth's surface

the weight force is $W = m_2 g$, it is less, because mass is invariant.
We refer to this as a *gravitational system*, and since weight force is a
variable, there is little to commend it as a base for a unit system.
Although the variation in g is negligible to three significant figures
and does not present a significant problem for engineering analysis
and design on the earth's surface, for a spacecraft in orbit the

variation in g would be large enough to be of concern, and under these conditions an absolute unit system would probably be required. The dimensions and units of the engineering fps system are shown in Table 7-5. Deriving a unit for mass, we have

$$F = ma$$

where

$$[F] = F \qquad [a] = \frac{L}{T^2}$$

Therefore

$$[m] = \frac{F}{a} = \frac{F}{L/T^2} = \frac{FT^2}{L}$$

The unit of mass is the *slug*, defined by

$$\text{Slug} = \text{lb}_f\text{-sec}^2/\text{ft}$$

Thus one slug is the amount of mass that a force of one pound will accelerate at the rate one foot per second per second.

example 7-7 What mass, in slugs, will receive an acceleration of 15.6 ft/sec^2 when acted upon by a force of 31.2 lb$_f$?

$$F = ma$$

$$m = \frac{F}{a} = \frac{31.2 \text{ lb}_f}{15.6 \text{ ft/sec}^2} = 2.00 \text{ lb}_f\text{-sec}^2/\text{ft} = 2.00 \text{ slugs}$$

The dimensions and unit systems we have discussed so far are summarized in Table 7-6.

table 7-5

Dimension	Unit	Abbreviation
Force F	Pound force	lb$_f$
Length L	Foot	ft
Time T	Second	sec

| | Absolute systems (MLT) | | | Gravitational systems (FLT) |
	MKS	CGS	British fps	Engineering fps
Fundamental dimensions				
Mass M	kg	g	lb_m	. . .
Length L	m	cm	ft	ft
Time T	sec	sec	sec	sec
Force F	. . .	. . .	. . .	lb_f
Derived dimensions				
Mass M	. . .	. . .	. . .	$lb_f\text{-}sec^2/ft$ = slug
Force F	$kg\text{-}m/sec^2$ = newton	$g\text{-}cm/sec^2$ = dyne	$lb_m\text{-}ft/sec^2$ = poundal	. . .

table 7-6 *Summary of dimension and unit systems*

units of heat and energy

Thus far we have been entirely concerned with the dimensions and units of mechanics. At this point let us make brief mention of the units of *heat* and *electricity*. As might be expected, there are several systems in use.

To define the concepts of heat in a *thermodynamic system* we need a fourth fundamental dimension, temperature. *Temperature* θ is the amount of heat, and its measure is based on highly reproducible constants of nature. The measure in present use is based on the triple point of water (see Table 7-1). Even though there is no known pure mechanical primary quantity which can be substituted for temperature, it can be related to energy. When temperature is combined with the fundamental mechanical units of force (or mass), length, and time, a completely new set of units can be formed. A more complete discussion of this system is found in advanced thermodynamics texts.

There are many systems of units for electricity and magnetism, all of which have a somewhat complicated background. They also require a fourth fundamental quantity in combination with the three fundamental mechanical dimensions. In the *electrostatic system* this fourth quantity is the *electric charge Q*. In another, the *electromagnetic system* the fourth quantity is defined as the *magnetic pole strength*. A complete description of these systems is beyond the scope of this text.

7-7 CONVERSION OF UNITS

A common problem in engineering is the necessity of converting to larger or smaller units within the same system or to units in another system. This deceptively simple process can lead to serious mistakes unless it is approached in a systematic mathematical manner. We have seen from the law of dimensional homogeneity that the dimensions of all the sums in an equation must be the same. Thus an equation such as

$$5a = 2b + 3c$$

where $[a] = L$ $[b] = L$ $[c] = L$

appears to be correct numerically as well as dimensionally. However, if the units of each term were shown, we might find that

$$5 \text{ ft} \neq 2 \text{ ft} + 3 \text{ in.}$$

Hence when the quantities in an equation are to be evaluated, each term in the equation must be expressed in the same units.

One technique for changing units in an expression is to multiply by a *conversion factor*, a ratio of equivalent magnitudes with a numerical value of 1. In this way the old unit cancels out, leaving the desired unit with the proper numerical coefficient. For example, to convert 100 ft to inches we would proceed as follows:

$$100 \text{ ft} = 100 \text{ ft} \times 12 \text{ in./ft} = 1,200 \text{ in.}$$

Here 12 in. = 1 ft, or 12 in./ft, is the conversion factor, since it is a ratio of equal measures and has a numerical value of 1. Conversion factors do not alter the value of an expression, but they do change the form of the units. Now for a more complicated example.

example 7-8   Convert the escape velocity 11.2 km/sec into miles per hour, using only the following conversion factors:

1 m = 3.28 ft   1 mile = 5,280 ft

1 hr = 3,600 sec   1 km = 1,000 m

Multiplication yields

$$v = \frac{11.2 \text{ km/sec} \times 1,000 \text{ m/km} \times 3.28 \text{ ft/m} \times 3,600 \text{ sec/hr}}{5,280 \text{ ft/miles}}$$

$$= 25,000 \text{ miles/hr}$$

Here the systematic mathematical and unit conversion proceeds concurrently.

Such problems are deceptively easy, and as a result they frequently receive only haphazard attention, which can lead to incorrect results.

example 7-9   A water department reported a domestic water consumption of 310 million gal/day. Using only the following conversion factors, convert this quantity into cubic feet per second and into tons per hour:

1 ft^3 = 7.48 gal

1 ft^3 of water = 62.5 lb

1 hr = 3,600 sec

1 day = 24 hr   1 ton = 2,000 lb$_f$

The number of cubic feet per second is

$$X = \frac{310,000,000 \text{ gal/day}}{7.48 \text{ gal/ft}^3 \times 24 \text{ hr/day} \times 3,600 \text{ sec/hr}} = 481 \text{ ft}^3/\text{sec}$$

The number of tons per hour is

$$X = \frac{310,000,000 \text{ gal/day} \times 62.5 \text{ lb/ft}^3}{7.48 \text{ gal/ft}^3 \times 24 \text{ hr/day} \times 2,000 \text{ lb/ton}} = 54,000 \text{ ton/hr}$$

Many of the commonly used abbreviations for units, such as psi for pounds per square inch, mph for miles per hour, and cfs for cubic feet per second, do not lend themselves to unit conversion and balancing and therefore are not recommended for such calculations.

7-8 MIXED OR AMBIGUOUS UNITS

Unfortunately in engineering practice it is not uncommon to find pound force and pound mass in the same expression. For example, pressure is frequently expressed as pound force per square foot and mass density as pound mass per cubic foot. When this situation occurs we say the equation has *mixed* or *inconsistent units*, because we are using a gravitational unit for force and an absolute unit for mass.

When mixed units are used in Newton's second law a constant other than unity must be employed. This is written

$$F = Kma$$

where $K = 1/g_c$ and $g_c = 32.2$, the acceleration due to gravity under standard conditions. Thus it is also customary to write Newton's second law as

$$F = \frac{1}{g_c} ma \qquad \qquad 7\text{-}1$$

when inconsistent units are involved. Solving Eq. 7-1 for the units of g_c yields

$$g_c = \frac{1}{F} ma = 1/\text{lb}_f \times \text{lb}_m \times \text{ft/sec}^2 = \text{lb}_m\text{-ft/lb}_f\text{-sec}^2$$

Hence

$$g_c = 32.2 \; \text{lb}_m\text{-ft/lb}_f\text{-sec}^2$$

which has no physical significance and is used only to balance Newton's second law.

There is a common misconception that all quantities having

the same physical dimensions must be of the same physical nature. While this is generally true, there are some notable exceptions. Consider the case of the physical quantities we call work and moment of a force. In the FLT system they both have the derived dimensions of FL, but they are very different physical quantities. As another example, in vector algebra dimensional analysis cannot distinguish the directional properties of vector quantities. It is possible in vector algebra to generate vector quantities with dimensions such as L^3 that are in no way indicative of the physical nature of the quantity.

Regardless of the system of units used, it is recommended that the engineer develop a habit of always checking the unit balance of all equations.

7-9 THE INTERNATIONAL SYSTEM OF UNITS

The United States is the only industrial nation that has not adopted some form of the metric measurement system used by more than 90 percent of the world's population. The British and Japanese governments are in the process of converting to metric measurement standards, and recently in the United States there has been a great deal of discussion and publicity about adoption of the metric system.

The plan that has received worldwide acceptance is the International System of Units (abbreviated SI, for Systeme International), which is an extension and a refinement of the traditional metric system. The SI was defined and adopted officially by the Eleventh General Conference on Weights and Measures, which met in Paris in October 1960. It is based on six fundamental dimensions shown in Table 7-7. All other units are derived from these six units.

Adoption of the SI in this country would end many of our present measurement ambiguities. For example, there would be one unit of mass, the kilogram, and one unit of force, the newton, which would be independent of the earth's gravity. Dimensionless numbers, such as the Mach, Reynolds, and Knudsen numbers,

Dimension	Unit	Abbreviation
Length	Meter	m
Mass	Kilogram	kg
Time	Second	s
Electric current	Ampere	A
Thermodynamic temperature	Degree Kelvin	°K
Luminous intensity	Candela	cd

table 7-7

would not be affected because these have the same value in any dimensional system. Other advantages of the system are its simplicity and the fact that it would reduce confusion among scientific disciplines.

Despite the obvious advantages in international trade, the major objection seems to be one of tradition and the cost of the changeover, particularly in the automotive, appliance, fastenings, and machine-tooling industries.

There is no doubt that our present illogical and antiquated measurement system is a liability in relations between engineering and science, industry and science, and the United States and other nations. Most knowledgeable people feel a changeover is not only inevitable, but must be made now.

SUMMARY

It is just as important to state the units of a measurement as its magnitude. A unit is the measure of a dimension, the character of the physical quantity itself. In mechanics all quantities can be expressed in terms of three fundamental dimensions, mass M or force F, length L, and time T. Scientists use a system based on mass and engineers use a system based on force. Quantities that result when we combine fundamental dimensions are called derived dimensions. A quantity that has no dimensions is called dimensionless or sterile.

According to the law of dimensional homogeneity, an expression or equation must balance dimensionally as well as numerically. Dimensional analysis is the process by which we derive information about the mathematical form of a physical relation by investigation of the dimensions.

Presently there are many systems of units to describe the physical variables resulting from measurements. A unit is a selected magnitude of a physical variable which serves as a basis of comparison to describe other magnitudes of the same variable. Some of the most important unit systems are the mks system, the cgs system, the British fps system, and the fps system. The engineering fps system is sometimes referred to as a gravitational system, since it is founded on *FLT* dimensions.

The United States is presently the only industrial nation that has not adopted some form of the metric system. It seems inevitable that we must abandon the obsolete measurement system still in use and adopt a modified metric system, the International System of Units, which is receiving worldwide acceptance.

PROBLEMS

7-1 In an *FLT* system what are the derived dimensions of
a Density (mass per volume)
b Angle
c Power
d Moment of force
e Stress (force per unit area)?

7-2 What are the derived dimensions in Prob. 7-1 in an *MLT* system?

7-3 Convert 500 in./sec to kilometers per week, where 1 m = 3.28 ft.

7-4 One horsepower is a measure of work being performed at the rate of 550 ft-lb$_f$/sec. How many foot–pounds force of work are done by a 100-hp motor working at its rated capacity for 3 hr?

7-5 Change 250 acres to square centimeters, using only the conversion factors

$$1 \text{ acre} = 43{,}560 \text{ ft}^2, \qquad 1 \text{ ft} = 12 \text{ in.} \qquad 1 \text{ in.} = 2.54 \text{ cm}$$

7-6 Change 515 cm³/sec of water to tons of water per hour, using only the conversion factors

$$1 \text{ in.} = 2.54 \text{ cm} \qquad 1 \text{ ton} = 2{,}000 \text{ lb}_f$$
$$1 \text{ ft}^3 \text{ of water} = 62.5 \text{ lb}_f \qquad 1 \text{ hr} = 3{,}600 \text{ sec}$$

7-7 It takes 365 days, 5 hr, 46 min, and 46 sec for the earth to make one complete trip around the sun. If the orbit is 5.84×10^8 miles, find the speed of the earth in meters per hour, where $1 \text{ m} = 3.28 \text{ ft}$.

7-8 In the dimensionally correct equation

$$p = 0.42 \left(\sin 2\theta + \frac{K}{L} \cos \theta \right) \frac{3w}{KgT^2}$$

where L = length

w = weight

g = acceleration

p = force per unit area

T = time

what are the units of K in the engineering fps gravitational system?

7-9 In the dimensionally correct formula

$$V = Ca \sqrt{\frac{2gh}{2 - (a/S)^2}}$$

where V = volume

a = area

g = acceleration

h = height

what are the units of C and S in the engineering fps gravitational system?

7-10 In Newton's law of gravitational attraction,

$$F = G \frac{m_1 m_2}{r^2}$$

where m_1, m_2 = masses

r = distance

F = force of attraction

G = gravitational constant

what are the dimensions of G in the MLT system? In the FLT system?

7-11 In the dimensionally correct equation

$$l = 2S \frac{8\pi}{g_1 - g_2} \left(14C - \frac{h + h_1}{2} \right)$$

where l = length

g = acceleration

h = length

what are the fundamental dimensions of S and C? Prove your answer by writing the equation in fundamental dimensions.

7-12 Determine if the equation

$$s = \frac{3a - 2b}{a} w \frac{b^2}{t^2}$$

where s = force per unit area

a, b = lengths

w = force per length

t = length

is dimensionally correct.

7-13   In the dimensionally correct equation

$$J = \frac{v^2 X}{g} (2m^2 \cos \theta - l^2)$$

where v = velocity

J = a force times a length

g = acceleration

m, l = lengths

what are the units of X in the engineering fps gravitational system? Prove your result.

7-14   Determine if the equation

$$s = \frac{p}{a} \left(2 + \frac{kl}{m^2} \right)$$

where s = a force per unit area

p = force

a = area

k, l, m = lengths

is dimensionally correct. Prove your answer by rewriting the equation in engineering fps gravitational units.

7-15   In the equation

$$p = \frac{37pv^2l}{gX^2} \left(\tan \theta + \frac{l}{X} \sin 4\theta \right)$$

where p = force

v = velocity

l = length

g = acceleration

what must be the fundamental dimension of X if the equation is to be dimensionally homogeneous?

7-16 Determine if the equation

$$s = p\,\frac{k^2 + a}{k^2 - a} + 2\pi p$$

where s, p = forces per unit area

a = area

k = length

is dimensionally correct. Prove your answer by rewriting the equation in engineering fps gravitational units.

7-17 In the dimensionally correct equation

$$t = r\left(\sqrt{\frac{4Ef + 3P}{4Ef - 5P}} - 4\right)$$

where t and r are lengths and E and P are forces, what are the fundamental dimensions of f?

7-18 Determine if the equation

$$s = -\frac{p}{\pi r t}\sin\theta + \sqrt{\frac{p^2}{a^2}}$$

where s = force per unit area

p = force

r, t = lengths

a = area

is dimensionally correct. Prove your answer by rewriting the equation in engineering fps gravitational units.

7-19 Is the following equation dimensionally correct?

$$pq = \frac{23wv^2}{gr}\left(\cos \alpha + \frac{r}{L}\cos 3\alpha\right) + (w - p)\tan \alpha$$

where p = force

q = a sterile value

w = weight

v = velocity

g = acceleration

r = length

and L = length

Prove your answer by rewriting the equation in FLT fundamental dimensions.

7-20 In the dimensionally correct equation

$$p = \left[(h - d)\left(h + \frac{d}{4}\right)y - y^3\right]\left[\frac{5wN}{hd^2(6 - f^2)}\right]$$

where h, d = lengths

p = force

w = weight

N = ratio of diameters

f = coefficient of friction

what are the units of y in the engineering fps gravitational system?

7-21 In the dimensionally homogeneous equation

$$\frac{p}{a} = \frac{5Eh^2}{(3 - \pi^2)d^6}\left[S^4 - (h - d)\left(h - \frac{d}{2}\right)S^2\right]$$

where

$$[p] = F \qquad [a] = L^2 \qquad [E] = \frac{F}{L^2}$$

$$[h] = L \qquad [d] = L$$

what are the dimensions of S in the FLT system?

7-22 Use the FLT system to solve for the fundamental dimensions of K and A in the dimensionally correct equation

$$PK = \frac{5E}{T} \left(6A^\bullet + \frac{4}{5} F \right) F^{2/5}$$

where P = power

E = energy

T = time

F = force

7-23 In the dimensionally homogeneous expression

$$\frac{4t}{V} = \left(4r - \frac{2}{5} b \right) b^{3/5} C$$

where t = time

V = volume

r, b = lengths

what must be the dimensions of C in the FLT system?

7-24 In the dimensionally correct equation

$$R = ml \frac{\sqrt{a/l^3 - 3}}{t^3 \sin \theta} + 4 \frac{S}{\omega}$$

where m = mass

l = length

t = time

θ = angle

ω = angular velocity

what are the dimensions of R, a, and S in the FLT system?

7-25   In the dimensionally correct equation

$$v = \sqrt{2A\left(\frac{p}{D} + \frac{vg}{2gr}\right)}$$

where v = velocity

p = pressure

D = mass per unit volume

g = acceleration

determine the dimensions of A and r in the FLT system.

7-26   Use the FLT system to find the dimensions of R and S and the value of n in the dimensionally homogeneous equation

$$\frac{R^n}{S} = \frac{2\pi p(\tau_1 - \tau_2)dAFM}{D(I \sin 2\theta)T^2} + \frac{pF^2Md}{A\pi \tan 3\theta \, T^2}$$

where p = pressure

τ = torque

d = diameter

A = area

F = force

M = mass

I = moment of interia, L^4

$\theta = 45°$

T = time

7-27 Use the *FLT* system to find the dimensions of *B*, *D*, and *E* and the values of exp *n* and exp *y* in the dimensionally correct equation

$$\frac{D^n}{B^y} = \left[357 \, \frac{Mpq}{F^4} \right]^4 + E$$

where *M* = mass

   p = pressure

   q = volume per time

   F = force

7-28 Use the *FLT* system to determine the dimensions of *X*, *Y*, and *Z* and the numerical values of the exponents *n* and *d* in the dimensionally correct equation

$$1112 \left(\frac{4MF^2 a}{1.5 \, ptB} \right)^3 = 417 \, \frac{X^n}{Y^d} + 695Z$$

where *M* = mass

   F = force

   p = pressure

   a = acceleration

   t = time

   B = area

7-29 What is the mass in pounds mass of an object which is being accelerated at 17.4 m/sec^2 by an unbalanced force of 1540 lb$_f$, where 1 m = 3.28 ft?

7-30 A satellite in orbit has a mass of 5,000 lb$_m$, where *g* is determined to be 15 ft/sec^2. What is its weight in pounds force at this point in its orbit?

7-31 A rocket resting on the moon's surface, where the acceleration due to gravity is 5.35 ft/sec², weighs 47,000 lb$_f$. What is its mass in slugs? In pounds mass? If the rocket is now returned to the earth's surface, where $g = 32.2$ ft/sec², what is its mass in slugs? What is its weight in pounds force?

7-32 Find the mass in slugs which is being accelerated at 13.7 m/sec² by an unbalanced force of 891 lb$_f$.

7-33 What is the mass, in pounds mass, that is being accelerated at 1.26 m/sec² by an unbalanced force of 252 lb$_f$?

7-34 What unbalanced force, expressed as pounds force, will accelerate a mass of 100 slugs at an acceleration of 450 cm/sec²?

7-35 Find the mass in slugs that will receive an acceleration of 35.2 m/min² when acted on by an unbalanced force of 75.3 lb$_f$.

7-36 If an unbalanced force of 873 lb$_f$ acts on a mass of 5.34 slugs, what acceleration, expressed as inches per second per second, will result?

7-37 The weight of the first Vanguard satellite on the earth's surface was 3.25 lb$_f$, while at the extreme position in its orbit its weight was found to be 1.23 lb$_f$.
- *a* What is its mass in pounds mass on the earth's surface?
- *b* What is its mass in slugs on the earth's surface?
- *c* What is its mass in pounds mass at the extreme position in its orbit?
- *d* What is the satellite's acceleration of gravity to the earth when it is in its extreme orbital position?

7-38 An antenna on the Surveyor that sent pictures of the moon's surface was found to have a weight of 100 lb$_f$ on the earth's surface.
- *a* What is its mass in pounds mass on the moon's surface, where $g = 5.35$ ft/sec²?

   b What is its mass in pounds mass on the earth's surface?

   c What is its mass in slugs on the earth's surface?

   d What unbalanced force, expressed as pounds force, is necessary to give it an acceleration of 47 ft/sec² on the moon's surface?

7-39 A phototelevision device on the Luna 12 was found to have a weight of 150 lb$_f$ on the earth's surface.

   a What is its mass in pounds mass on the moon's surface, where $g = 5.35$ ft/sec²?

   b What is its mass in pounds mass on the earth's surface?

   c What is its mass in slugs on the earth's surface?

   d What unbalanced force, expressed as pounds force, is necessary to give it an acceleration of 15 m/sec² on the moon's surface?

7-40 It has been estimated that 120,000 lb$_m$ of equipment will be needed to sustain six men on a lunar outpost for 90 days, where $g = 5.35$ ft/sec².

   a What is the weight of this equipment, expressed as pounds force, on the earth's surface?

   b What is the weight of this equipment, expressed as pounds force, on the moon's surface?

   c What is the mass of this equipment, expressed as pounds mass on the moon's surface?

   d How many slugs of mass does this equipment represent on the moon's surface?

   e What unbalanced force, expressed as pounds force, is necessary to give one-tenth of this mass an acceleration of 10 m/sec²?

7-41 The 36-story Saturn V Apollo spacecraft had a weight of 6.2 million lb$_f$ at Cape Kennedy. To launch this vehicle required rocket engines that developed 7.5 million lb$_f$ of thrust (force) at liftoff.

   a What acceleration, expressed as feet per second per second, will this thrust give the craft at liftoff?

    b If the payload had a mass of 284,000 lb_m, what would be its weight in pounds force at a point in the orbit where $g = 25.0 \text{ ft/sec}^2$?

    c What would be the mass of the payload in slugs at the same point in the orbit?

7-42 The 23-ft-tall lunar module built to land on the moon and then blast off again weighs 32,000 lb_f at Cape Kennedy. What force, expressed as pounds force, is necessary to give the vehicle an acceleration of 1.70 ft/sec^2 at blastoff from the moon's surface, where $g = 5.35 \text{ ft/sec}^2$?

7-43 The photographic equipment on Luna 9 that transmitted pictures of the moon's surface was said to have a mass of 0.108 slugs on the earth's surface.

    a What is its mass in pounds mass on the earth's surface?

    b What is its weight in pounds force on the earth's surface?

    c What unbalanced force, expressed as pounds force, is necessary to give it an acceleration of 1.84 m/sec^2?

    d What is its mass in pounds mass on the moon's surface, where $g = 5.35 \text{ ft/sec}^2$?

7-44 The weight of a satellite on the earth's surface was 10.7 lb_f, while at the extreme position in its orbit its weight was found to be 4.23 lb_f.

    a What is its mass in pounds mass on the earth's surface?

    b What is its mass expressed in slugs on the earth's surface?

    c What is its mass in pounds mass at the extreme position in its orbit?

    d What is the satellite's acceleration of gravity to the earth when it is in its extreme position in its orbit?

7-45 If 5 slugs of mass weighs 64.5 lb_f on the planet Mars and 434 lb_f on the planet Jupiter, what is the acceleration due to gravity on the surface of Mars and on Jupiter?

7-46 The Lunar Orbiter 2 was said to have a mass of 26.4 slugs on the earth.

  a What is its weight in pounds force on the earth?

  b What is its mass in pounds mass on the moon's surface, where $g = 5.35$ ft/sec^2?

  c What unbalanced force, expressed as pounds force, is necessary to give it an acceleration of 923 cm/min^2?

appendixes

A SPECIFICATIONS FOR ENGINEERING COMPUTATIONS

A-1 ANALYSIS OF AN ENGINEERING PROBLEM

The perfect solution to a physical problem is never attainable. This is because the data are either inadequate or incomplete, there are measurement errors, there are limitations to the mathematical tools, there are time and financial restrictions, and of necessity the solution may be based on assumptions. However, the engineer's idealized or approximate solution, while not exact, has proved to be workable, economical, and safe. All engineering calculations must eventually be presented to other persons, either for checking or for communication of the results, and to be understandable they must be shown in a neat and orderly manner. A neat, logical, and systematic presentation indicates the same qualities in the solution itself.

True engineering situations are seldom as clearly defined as textbook problems, but once the method of problem analysis has been mastered, it is easily extended to more complex real-life situations. For this reason it is important to approach even the direct and limited problems in textbooks in a professional and workmanlike manner. Generally the problem-solving procedure, which with only slight modifications is the engineering design process, follows a basic format:*

problem definition
Determine what the problem is and its extent; this is the logical first step in the solution of any problem. Never proceed with a solution until you have clearly identified the problem.

data analysis
Determine what data are available and what parts are pertinent to the problem at hand. Occasionally there is too much information, and the extraneous data must be sorted out and discarded. Any assumptions that must be made should be clearly noted as such.

*Robert Q. Brown, "Introduction to Engineering Problems," Prentice-Hall, Inc., Englewood Cliffs, N.J., 1948.

Photos at left show failure of the first Tacoma Narrows bridge. Design was adequate as a static structure, but winds produced severe aerodynamic effects. Courtesy of *The Trend in Engineering*, University of Washington.

problem solution

Determine the law or principle upon which the solution is to be based and express it symbolically before you substitute the actual values and proceed with the calculations.

identification of results

The most important part of the solution is the result or answer; thus it should be conspicuously displayed and identified. This is usually done by underlining and then indexing to the right-hand margin. Be sure the answer has both a numerical and unit result.

analysis of results

It is customary to have a second person check and analyze all engineering computations. In addition, the engineer should check his own work as he proceeds with the solution. Always check the answer to see if it looks reasonable and examine it in the light of the assumptions made. If there is any doubt about its validity, a complete reexamination of the problem should be made.

A-2   ENGINEERING COMPUTATIONS FORMAT

Engineering calculations must be neatly and systematically arranged; they must be clear; they must be accurate and they must be understandable to other knowledgeable people. The work should be done on good quality paper or engineering-school problem sheets. Each page of calculations should have a heading which includes the course number, the date, your name, the problem number, and the number of the sheet, as shown in Fig. A-1. All lettering should be done in a professional style on one side of the paper. All calculations should be shown in full. If you cannot do a calculation in your head, then show it in full on the calculation sheet, so that it can be checked. Do not use scratch sheets. Do not crowd the work.

A properly labeled sketch or diagram of the problem usually can materially help in the solution. These sketches should be

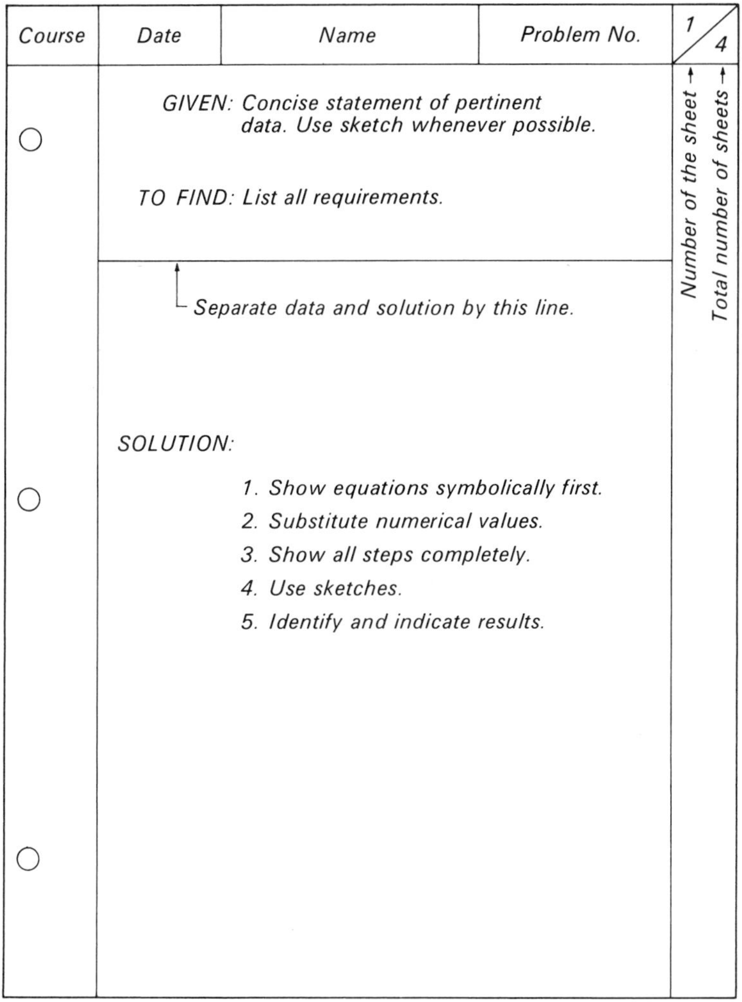

Course	Date	Name	Problem No.	1 / 4

GIVEN: Concise statement of pertinent
data. Use sketch whenever possible.

TO FIND: List all requirements.

Number of the sheet →

Total number of sheets →

⌐ Separate data and solution by this line.

SOLUTION:

1. Show equations symbolically first.
2. Substitute numerical values.
3. Show all steps completely.
4. Use sketches.
5. Identify and indicate results.

figure *A-1   Arrangement of problem sheet*

Course	Date	Name	Problem No.	1/1

○

GIVEN: A random sample of the diameters
of a machine shaft production by
a certain manufacturing firm
revealed $\bar{X} = 1.5750$ in. and $\sigma_s = 0.0055$ in.

TO FIND: If shafts having diameters between
1.5662 and 1.5838 in. are acceptable,
what is percentage of rejects?

SOLUTION:

$$\begin{array}{r} 1.5750 \\ -1.5662 \\ \hline 0.0088 \end{array}$$

$$Z_1 = \frac{\bar{X}_1 - \bar{X}}{\sigma_s} = \frac{1.5750 - 1.5662}{0.0055} = \frac{0.0088}{0.0055} = 1.6$$

○

$$\begin{array}{r} 1.5838 \\ -1.5750 \\ \hline 0.0088 \end{array}$$

$$Z_2 = \frac{1.5838 - 1.5750}{0.0055} = 1.6$$

From Table 5-3
Rejects = 10.96% ◄———— Ans.

○

Z_1 | Z_2
1.5750
1.5662   1.5838

figure A -2   Arrangement of solution

sufficiently large and neatly drawn so that known values in the problem can be displayed. A typical problem solution is shown in Fig. A-2.

A-3   SPECIFICATIONS FOR ENGINEERING COMPUTATIONS

Following are some suggestions concerning workmanship and style that will meet professional engineering standards. Undoubtedly there will be variations in different industries and areas of engineering, but these items represent good engineering practice. They are presented at random, and not in any order of importance.

1   Always use pencil.

2   Use horizontal fraction lines; fractions should appear as $5\frac{3}{8}$, *not* as 5 3/8.

3   Show exponents and subscripts clearly.

4   Show decimal figures less than unity with a zero before the decimal point; use 0.58, *not* .58.

5   Divide the problem into its logical parts by horizontal lines across the page.

6   Show addition and subtraction in vertical columns rather than horizontal rows; thus

$$
\begin{array}{r}
15.1 \\
0.9 \\
210.3 \\
\underline{98.2}
\end{array}
\qquad not \qquad 15.1 + 0.9 + 210.3 + 98.2
$$

7   Use the sign $\times$, not the dot, for multiplication of figures; that is, 4×5, *not* $4 \cdot 5$.

8   Show all units.

9   Do not mix units.

10   Do not use radicals in answers.

11   Separate different problems on the same sheet by two continuous horizontal lines.

B SIGNIFICANT FIGURES

B-1 DEFINITION OF SIGNIFICANT FIGURES

Since all measurements contain errors and ultimately require some kind of a readout from a graduated scale, it is important to read and record the correct number of digits in the observation. Valuable time may be wasted in making calculations based on measurements that have more digits than are warranted by the sensitivity of the measuring device. Even when the measurement data are shown to the proper number of digits, the computations may be carried to an excessive number of significant figures. Some confusion is also caused by the failure to distinguish between exact numbers or counts and numbers which result from measured quantities. The objective is to give the maximum information about the measurement without introducing misinformation.

In making a measurement it is considered good practice to read and record all digits from the graduated scale, plus one estimated digit. These are the *significant figures*. It is not considered proper procedure to estimate more than one digit. For example, on the pH meter shown in Fig. B-1 the needle clearly shows a point greater than 6 but less than 7, and so we can without question record the first digit in the reading as 6. Closer observation reveals that the needle has stopped at a point that is greater than 6.3 but less than 6.4, and so we can safely note the second digit and say that the reading is 6.3. However, very close inspection reveals that the

figure B-1 *A pH meter*

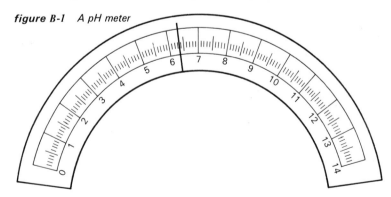

Measurement	Significant figures	Comments
45.1	Three	Decimal point does not determine significant figures
4.51	Three	Decimal point does not determine significant figures
0.451	Three	Decimal point does not determine significant figures
0.00451	Three	Decimal point does not determine significant figures
4.51×10^8	Three	Decimal point does not determine significant figures
0.037	Two	Decimal point does not determine significant figures
0.0370	Two or three	Confusing; may contain two or three significant figures
0.00008	One	
5,255	Four	
3,400	Two, three, or four	Confusing; may contain two, three or four significant figures
75.0	Three	Zero is significant in this case because it could just as well be omitted for proper location of decimal point

table B-1   Examples of significant figures

needle is not at 6.3 or at 6.4, but somewhere in between. By estimation the needle is read as being about four-tenths of the distance between the 6.3 and 6.4 graduations, and so it would be proper to report the result as 6.34. Since this measurement contains two digits that can be read from the graduated scale without question, plus one that is estimated, it contains *three* significant figures. An over-zealous observer might be tempted to report a result of, say, 6.342; this "accuracy" would be fictitious. Some examples of significant figures are shown in Table B-1.

B-2   USE OF SIGNIFICANT FIGURES

To avoid ambiguity, in using measurements the rules and conventions that have been adopted in engineering design and analysis should be thoroughly understood.

rounding off

In rounding off to the desired number of significant figures, the last digit to be retained is increased by one if the first digit dropped is greater than 5; for example,

5.386 becomes 5.39, which becomes 5.4
0.09786 becomes 0.0979, which becomes 0.098

If the digit to be dropped is less than 5, the preceding digit is left unchanged; for example,

5.213 becomes 5.21, which becomes 5.2
0.04432 becomes 0.0443, which becomes 0.044

If the digit to be dropped is just 5, the preceding digit is rounded to the nearest *even* number; for example,

24.475 becomes 25.48, which becomes 25.5
31.225 becomes 31.22, which becomes 31.2
7.3345 becomes 7.334, which becomes 7.33
7.3452 becomes 7.345, which becomes 7.34

The procedure for rounding off a single digit also applies to the rounding off of several digits. Thus when two, three, or four digits are to be rounded the above rules apply, but the controlling criterion is whether the digits to be dropped are greater than, less than, or equal to 50, 500, and 5,000, respectively. It should be noted that results for rounding off in single-digit steps may occasionally differ from those for rounding off in multiple-digit steps. For example, if the measurement 16.501 were to be rounded to two significant figures in one-digit steps, it would be 16; in a three-digit step it would be 17.

Generally it is desirable to round off at the completion of the calculations. It may be argued that the nonsignificant digits should be dropped before subsequent computations are made, but generally dropping the nonsignificant digits usually increases the uncertainty.

addition and subtraction

When obtaining the sum or difference of a set of measurements no columns containing non-significant figures should be added or subtracted. In other words, do not add or subtract columns that contain doubtful figures, as in the following examples:

```
  23.15                 234.1245
   2.223                  1.523
+  4.2                 + 24.230
  -----                  -------
  29.5                  259.877
    ▲                        ▲
```

This column contains the first doubtful digit, and so we are not justified in adding the columns to the right of it.

```
 353.1257                45.097
- 42.9                  - 5.4
 --------                ------
 310.2                   39.6
     ▲                      ▲
```

This column contains the first doubtful digit, and so we are not justified in subtracting the columns to the right of it.

Sometimes it may be desirable in addition and subtraction to round off all the measurements such that they have one more significant figure than the column containing the first doubtful digit. For example, consider the addition of the following measurements:

```
   43.45              43.45              43.45
  110.034            110.034            110.03
   14.2               14.2               14.2
+   0.0967          +   0.0967         +   0.10
  --------           --------           ------
  167.7807           167.6              167.78
```

Without regard to significant figures	By addition rule	By rounding first

As in all engineering calculations, evaluation of these results requires experience and judgment. The engineer must be aware of the significance of the data from which the results were generated and try to determine their validity in light of the assumptions made.

multiplication and division

The product or quotient of a multiplication or division operation must not contain any more significant figures than the term in the operation that has the lowest number of significant figures. Consider the following examples:

$33.198 \times 1.43 = 47.47314$, which should be reported as 47.5

$27.125 \times 0.021 = 0.569625$, which should be reported as 0.57

$632.10 \div 0.03 = 21{,}070$, which should be reported as 2×10^4

Sometimes, to expedite the multiplication or division, the numbers are first rounded off to one more digit than that in the measurement with the least number of significant figures. The final product or quotient is then rounded off to the same number of significant figures as the term that has the least number of significant figures. Let us again consider the previous examples:

$33.198 \times 1.43 = 33.20 \times 1.43 = 47.4760$, which should be reported as 47.5

$27.125 \times 0.021 = 27.1 \times 0.021 = 0.5691$, which should be reported as 0.57

$632.10 \div 0.03 = 6.3 \times 10^2 \div 0.03 = 2.1 \times 10^4$, which should be reported 2×10^4

B-3 AMBIGUOUS ZEROS

The significance of a zero in a measurement depends on its location with reference to the other digits. It is impossible to distinguish the number of significant figures in measurements written as 5,000, 19,000, or 200.

If a zero appears at the end of a number, it is significant only if it actually represents a reliable measured value. Thus if a velocity is measured to the nearest mile per hour and is recorded as 130 mph, then the zero is significant and the number 130 has three significant figures. Since the zero in this case may be ambiguous, this number should be recorded instead in scientific notation as 1.30×10^2 mph.

The zero is not significant when it is used mainly as a spacer for the decimal point, because these zeros are not read from the graduated scale of the measuring device. Thus there are three significant figures in 0.000922, two in 0.025 and one in 0.000004.

Note again that the decimal point does not establish the number of significant figures.

The zero is significant if it is both preceded and followed by nonzero digits. Hence 4.7003 contains five significant figures, 3.054 contains four, and 0.0909 has three.

B-4 SCIENTIFIC NOTATION

Most of the confusion concerning the number of significant figures in measurements can be eliminated by the use of scientific notation. The procedure is to reduce the measurement to a number between 1 and 10, with the proper number of significant figures, and locate the decimal point by a power of 10. This also has the advantage of making the number easier to handle. Consider the following examples:

To express 15,000 with three significant figures use 1.50×10^4
To express 15,000 with two significant figures use 1.5×10^4
To express 0.005094 with three significant figures use
5.09×10^{-3}
To express 0.005094 with two significant figures use
5.1×10^{-3}
To express 2,500,000 with four significant figures use
2.500×10^6

B-5 NUMBERS WITH UNLIMITED SIGNIFICANT FIGURES

Frequently engineering computations contain measurements, numbers that are exact, and numbers that have unlimited significant figures. Consider the simple problem of computing the circumference of a circle after we have measured the radius. The familiar formula is

$$c = 2\pi r$$

where c is the circumference and r is the radius. The value of π, which is a ratio of the circumference to the diameter, can of course be computed to any number of significant figures. The number 2 in the formula is an exact count, and so it contains an unlimited number of significant figures. If the radius is measured as 2.12 in., then the circumference could be computed as

$$c = 2.00 \times 3.14 \times 2.12 = 13.3 \text{ in.}$$

Note that the controlling factor in determining the number of significant figures in the circumference is the measurement of the radius, because the factor 2 and π both contain as many significant figures as needed. Another example of a term with an unlimited number of significant figures is e, the base of Naperian logarithms (2.718). Exact numbers in formulas, even though they may be shown as a single digit, carry by implication as many significant figures as necessary in the mathematical operation.

B-6   SPECIAL CASES

Occasionally an extra significant figure in the result is justified. Consider the multiplication

$$3.0 \times 2.5 = 7.5$$

This follows our rule with no problem. However, in the multiplication

$$4.0 \times 2.5 = 10.0$$

we see that the two multipliers contain two significant figures, but the product probably can be shown, as indicated, with three significant figures. While this seemingly violates the rule, it is usually justified when none of the measurements in the calculation begins with the digit 1 but the result begins with 1.

The number 9 is almost a two-digit number, and hence an extra significant figure is sometimes justified. If we multiply 9.87 by 4.0721, an extra digit may be warranted in the product because it could be argued that 9.87 has almost four significant figures. Thus

$$9.87 \times 4.0721 = 40.19$$

C SLIDE-RULE HINTS

C-1 INTRODUCTION TO THE SLIDE RULE

Generally freshmen engineering students have some knowledge of the slide rule. However, even those who are quite proficient in its use often have difficulty with decimal-point location. The hints presented here should help to reduce mistakes in slide-rule computations. Basic familiarity with the slide rule and its scale readings is assumed. Our discussion will concern only the most common slide-rule scale arrangements; many variations to these exist, but the principles remain the same.

The construction and operation of the slide rule is based on the theory of logarithms.* Recall that the *logarithm* of a number to a given base is the power of the base required to give the number. Thus with logarithms to the base 10, the power necessary to raise the base 10 to 100 is 2; hence the logarithm of 100 would be 2.000. The logarithm is made up of two parts, the characteristic and mantissa.

characteristic of logarithms

The *characteristic* is a whole number that may be positive, negative, or zero, which is obtained by inspection to determine the decimal point. The characteristic is determined in accordance with the following rules:

For numbers greater than 1 the characteristic is one less than the number of digits to the left of the decimal point and is always positive.

For numbers less than 1 the characteristic is one more than the number of ciphers between the decimal point and the first digit and is always negative.

Note that the characteristic is equal to the power of 10 in scientific notation, where the number is expressed as a single digit, a decimal point, the remaining digits, and the power of 10. Some examples are shown in Table C-1.

*Those who are not thoroughly familiar with logarithms should consult a mathematics text.

Number	Characteristic	Power-of-10 notation
373	2	3.73×10^2
97,500	4	9.75×10^4
5.37	0	$5.37 \times 10^\circ$
0.0147	-2	1.47×10^{-2}
0.000956	-4	9.56×10^{-4}

table C-1

the mantissa

The *mantissa*, a decimal that is always positive, determines the sequence of digits and may be obtained from log tables. Since a logarithm is an exponent, it obeys the following laws:

$$a^n a^m = a^{n+m}$$

$$a^n/a^m = a^{n-m}$$

$$(a^n)^m = a^{nm}$$

Here we see that the use of logs changes the tedious operations of multiplication and division into addition and subtraction, respectively. To further simplify the operation the slide rule enables us to add or subtract these logs graphically. The slide rule, then, is a graphic logarithm table, with the mantissas laid out to scale on the rule. The characteristics of the logs must be added or subtracted mentally.

C-2   MULTIPLICATION AND DIVISION ON THE SLIDE RULE

multiplication

The slide rule multiplies two numbers by graphical addition of their logarithms, where the mantissas of the logs of the numbers are represented by distances on the slide rule. For example, to multiply 2×3 on the slide rule we use the C and D scales, as shown in Fig. C-1. In a simple problem such as this the decimal point is obvious. To demonstrate the procedure for more complicated problems we indicate the characteristic above each term:

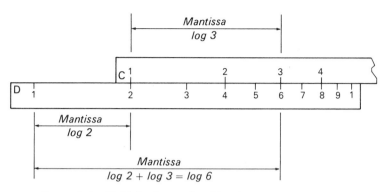

figure C-1   Multiplication on the slide rule

$$0 \qquad 0 \rightarrow 0 + 0 = 0$$
$$2 \times 3 = \quad 6$$

Since the slide rule graphically adds the mantissas, to obtain the characteristic of the answer we must add the individual characteristics algebraically. Consider the following problems, which use the same slide-rule setup shown in Fig. C-1:

$$-4 \qquad\quad -3 \longrightarrow -4 + (-3) = -7$$
$$0.0002 \times 0.003 = \quad 6 \times 10^{-7}$$

$$\qquad\qquad\qquad -4 \longrightarrow 8 + (-4) = 4$$
$$2 \times 10^8 \times 0.0003 = \quad 6 \times 10^4$$

All problems can be worked this way.

In addition, it is recommended that an estimate be made of the answer as a check. For example, suppose we are to multiply

$$0.288 \times 11.98 \times 23.3$$

For an estimate we rewrite the terms by rounding off and get the approximate answer

$$0.3 \times 12 \times 23 = 3.6 \times 23 = 80 \text{ approx.}$$

By slide rule a more accurate answer would be

$$-1 \qquad\quad 1 \qquad\quad 1 \longrightarrow (-1) + 1 + 1 = 1$$
$$0.288 \times 11.98 \times 23.3 = \qquad 80.1$$

Our approximate answer provides a check on the slide-rule decimal-point location in the answer.

division

With the slide rule division is accomplished by graphical subtraction of logarithms. For example, to divide 7.5 by 2.5 we would use the slide-rule setup shown in Fig. C-2. Again, with a simple problem such as this the decimal is obvious; the complete procedure is

$$0 \longrightarrow 0 - 0 = 0$$
$$\frac{7.5}{2.5} = \quad 3$$
$$0$$

Now consider the following quotients, with the same slide-rule setting as indicated in Fig. C-2.

$$\overrightarrow{} 6 - (-3) = 6 + 3 = 9$$
$$\frac{7.5 \times 10^6}{0.0025} = \quad 3 \times 10^9$$
$$-3$$

$$-3 \longrightarrow -3 - 5 = -8$$
$$\frac{0.0075}{2.5 \times 10^5} = \quad 3 \times 10^{-8}$$

figure C -2   *Division on the slide rule*

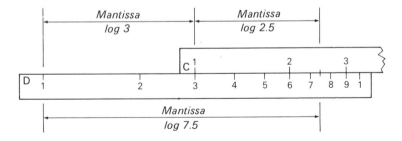

projection rule for multiplication

Frequently in multiplication the sum of the mantissas is greater than one scale length on the rule. When this happens it is necessary to place the right index of the C scale over one of the multipliers on the *D* scale; the hairline is then brought over the number representing the mantissa of the other multiplier, and the answer is read under the hairline on the fixed D scale. Suppose we want to multiply 3 × 6. Placing the characteristics above each term and multiplying, we have

0   0 ———→ 0 + 0 = 0
3 × 6 ≠   1.8

Here we see that for the correct decimal point we must add 1 to the characteristic because the sum of the mantissas is greater than 1. By adding the 1 we get the correct result

0   0 + 1 ———→ 0 + 0 + 1 = 1
3 × 6 =   18

We may state the projection rule for multiplication as follows:

Each time the left index of the C scale extends to the left of the index of the D scale, add 1 to the characteristic of the logarithm of the multiplier that caused the index to project.

projection rule for division

When the divisor is larger than the dividend the left index of the C scale will extend beyond the left of the D scale index. For example, in dividing 4 by 8,

0 ———→ 0 − 0 = 0
$$\frac{4}{8} \neq \quad 5$$
0

Here again we see that for the correct decimal point we must add 1 to the characteristic of the term causing the projection—in this case the 8,

$$0 \longrightarrow 0 - 1 = -1$$

$$\underset{0 + 1}{\frac{4}{8}} = 0.5$$

The projection rule for division is stated as:

Each time the left index of the C scale extends to the left of the left index of the D scale, add 1 to the characteristic of the logarithm of the term which caused the index to project.

combined multiplication and division

Most engineering calculations entail both multiplication and division. In such cases fewer settings of the slide are required if the multiplication and division operations are alternated, by the so-called *crisscross* or *zigzag* method. If the division is done first, the index of the C scale is automatically in place for the succeeding multiplication, and so on. The projection rule for both multiplication and division is applicable in these combined operations. Consider a problem such as the following:

$$
\begin{array}{c}
0 \qquad\quad 5 + 1 \longrightarrow 6 \qquad 6 - (-2) = 6 + 2 = 8 \\
\dfrac{3.29 \times 953,000}{0.0637 \times 5.35 \times 10^{-2}} = 9.2 \times 10^{8} \\
-2 + 1 \qquad\quad -2 + 1 \longrightarrow -2
\end{array}
$$

When the operations are carried out in the order indicated by the arrows, the $+1$ are the result of projections of the C scale to the left of the D scale.

Remember that in multiplication and division the answer is always read from the fixed scale.

C-3 SQUARES AND SQUARE ROOTS

On some slide rules the A scale has been constructed so that it is one-half as long as the D scale; thus there are two complete logarithmic scales on the A scale whose total length equals that of the D scale. Setting a number on the D scale and reading it on the A scale is then equivalent to multiplying the log of the number by 2, or squaring the number. The reverse operation would give the square root of a number. On other slide rules the scales marked R1 and R2 or Sq1 and Sq2 are made twice as long as the D scale, and these are used for squares and square roots. In this case a number is set on the R_1 or R_2 scale and its square is read on the D scale. The characteristic method of decimal-point location applies for powers.

decimal-point location for squares

The rules for decimal-point location are as follows:

1 If the answer falls on the left (first) section of the A scale (or if the R_1 scale is used), multiply the characteristic of the term to be squared by 2.

2 If the answer falls on the right (second) section of the A scale (or if the R_2 scale is used), multiply the characteristic of the term to be squared by 2 and add 1.

For example; the square of 0.0253 is

$$-2 \longrightarrow 2 \times (-2) = -4$$
$$0.0253^2 = \quad 6.4 \times 10^{-4}$$

since the answer was obtained on the left portion of the A scale. The square of 535 is

$$2 \longrightarrow 2 \times 2 + 1 = 5$$
$$535^2 = 2.86 \times 10^5$$

Because the answer fell on the right section of the A scale, we have added 1 to the characteristic.

decimal-point location for square roots

In this operation we find it convenient to resort to a technique used in the longhand extraction of the square root, in which we marked off the number in groups of twos, starting at the decimal point. We noted that there was one figure in the root for each group or partial group of two in the number. Also, for numbers less than 1 there was one cipher in the root for every pair of ciphers in the number. There are two possible slide-rule settings for finding the square root, and this procedure indicates which section of the A scale to use. When the group farthest to the left contains one digit we use the left section, and when it contains two digits we use the right section on the A scale. Thus

There is one digit in the root for each pair in the number.

$$\sqrt{75\ 30\ 00} = 869$$

Two digits here tells us that we use the right portion of the A scale.

and

There is one cipher in the root for each pair of ciphers in the number.

$$0.00\ 00\ 08\ 35^{\frac{1}{2}} = 0.00289$$

One digit here tells us that we use the left portion of the A scale.

An estimate of the answer should always be made as a check.

C-4   CUBES AND CUBE ROOTS

On most slide rules there is a scale marked K which is made up of three complete logarithmic scales whose total length is equal to that of the D scale. Thus if a number is set on the D scale and read on the K scale, the log has been multiplied by 3 and the result is the cube of the number. The cube root is obtained by the reverse procedure.

decimal-point location for cubes

The rules for decimal-point location are as follows:

1 If the answer appears on the first (left) section of the K scale, multiply the characteristic of the term to be cubed by 3.

2 If the answer appears on the second (middle) section of the K scale, multiply the characteristic of the term to be cubed by 3 and add 1.

3 If the answer appears on the third (right) section of the K scale, multiply the characteristic of the term to be cubed by 3 and add 2.

For example, the cube of 19.5 is

$$1 \longrightarrow 3 \times 1 = 3$$
$$19.5^3 = 7.42 \times 10^3$$

since the answer fell on the first (left) section of K scale. The cube of 0.00358 is

$$-3 \longrightarrow 3 \times (-3) = -9 + 1 = -8$$
$$0.00358^3 = \quad 4.6 \times 10^{-8}$$

Because the answer fell on the second (middle) portion of the K scale, 1 has been added to the characteristic. The cube of 7.17 × 10^7 is

$$\longrightarrow 3 \times 7 = 21 + 2 = 23$$
$$(7.17 \times 10^7)^3 = \quad 3.7 \times 10^{23}$$

Because the answer fell on the third (right) portion of the K scale, 2 has been added to the characteristic.

decimal-point location for cube roots

Since there are three possible settings on the slide rule for the cube root, we again resort to a technique used in the longhand extraction of the cube root to determine the correct section of the K scale to use. We mark off the number in groups of three, starting at the decimal point; when the group farthest to the left contains one digit we use the left (first section; when it contains two digits we use the center (second) section; when it contains three digits we use the right (third) section. Also, there will be one digit in the root for every group or partial group of three digits in the number. For decimals less than 1 there will be one cipher in the root for every group of three ciphers in the number. For decimals less than 1 there will be one cipher in the root for every group of three ciphers in the number.

Consider the following examples:

$8\ 590^{\frac{1}{3}} = 20.5$

There is one digit in the cube root for each group or partial group of three in the number.

One digit here tells us we use the left (first) section of the K scale.

$(0.000\ 000\ 073)^{\frac{1}{3}} = 0.0042$

There is one cipher in the cube root for each group of three ciphers in the number; the digits from the slide rule then follow in order.

Two digits here tells us we use the center (second) section of the K scale.

$(383,000)^{\frac{1}{3}} = 73$

There is one digit in cube root for every three in the number.

Three digits here tells us we use the right (third) section of the K scale.

On certain other slide rules there are three separate cube-root scales instead of a K scale. These cube-root scales are used in conjunction with the D scale to obtain cubes and cube roots. The process is just the reverse from that described above.

C-5   TRIGONOMETRIC OPERATIONS

The slide rule may be used to determine trigonometric functions of angles. We will discuss only the sine, cosine, and tangent functions, since the other trigonometric functions are derivable from these.

sine scale (S scale)

On this scale the graduations represent angles in degrees. The subdivisions may be either minutes or tenths of degrees. Actually there are two scales on the S scale, one for sines and one for cosines. On the sine scale the numerals to the right of the marks represent angles that increase from left to right. On the cosine scale (not marked as such) the numerals to the left of the marks represent angles that increase from right to left. To find the sine or cosine function we set the angle on S scale (sine or cosine) and read the result on the C or D scale. Note that if the D scale is used, the S and D scales must be aligned. Since sin 90° = 1.00 and cos 0° = 1.00, the decimal point must be placed in front of the digits read from the scale for functions of angles less than 90°. Examples are shown in Fig. C-3.

figure C-3   *Operations on the S scale*

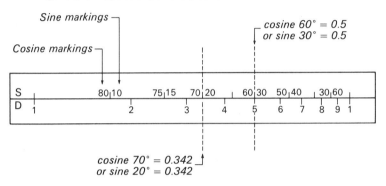

cosine 70° = 0.342
or sine 20° = 0.342

figure C-4   *Operations on the T scale*

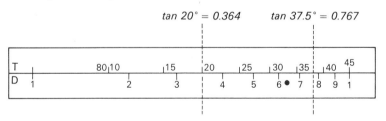

figure C-5   *Operations on the ST scale*

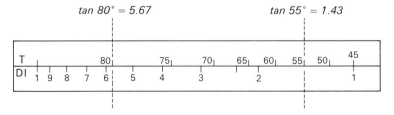

tangent scale (T scale)

This scale also has numerical markings on each side of the graduations. The numerals on the right increase from left to right, and the numerals on the left increase from right to left (see Fig. C-4). To obtain the tangent function for angles $5.74°$ to $45°$ we set the angle on the T scale and read the function on the C or D scale if it is aligned with the T scale. Since the tangent of $45°$ is equal to 1, the decimal point must be placed in front of the digits read. For angles $45°$ to $84.3°$ the answer must be read on the DI or CI scales and will be a value greater than 1. See Figs. C-4 and C-5 for some examples.

sine tangent (ST) scale

For angles less than $5.74°$ the numerical values of sine and tangent expressed to three significant figures are essentially the same. Thus the one scale marked ST will suffice for both functions. To obtain these functions we set the angles on the ST scale and read the value on the C or D scale. Since the sine of $5.74°$ is equal to 0.1, it follows that for smaller angles a cipher must be placed in front of the digits read to obtain the correct decimal place.

The trigonometric slide-rule operations are summarized in Table C-2 for quick reference.

table C-2   *Summary of trigonometric operations on the slide rule*

Function	Range in angle, deg
Sine or tangent	0–0.574
Sine or tangent	0.574–5.74
Sine	5.74–90
Cosine	0–84.26
Tangent	84.26–89.4
Cosine	84.26–89.4
Tangent	5.74–45
Tangent	45–84.26

C-6   LOG-LOG SCALES

logarithm of a number

To obtain the mantissa of the logarithm (base 10) of numbers we set the number on the D scale and read the mantissa on the L scale. As always, the characteristic is determined by inspection. Thus

$$\log = 7,530 = 3.\underset{\underset{\text{Obtained by inspection}}{\blacktriangle}}{\overset{\overset{\blacktriangledown \text{ Obtained from } L \text{ scale}}{\frown}}{877}}$$

The use of log-log scales enables us to raise a number to a decimal or fractional power as easily as performing simple multi-plication or division. Three pairs of matched or mated scales— LL1 → LL01, LL2 → LL02, and LL3 → LL03—are used in con-junction with the C and D scales. Each division on these scales represents a single unique number, and the scales have the ranges shown in Table C-3. Thus the scales represent a continuous range of numbers from 1.01 to 22,026 and from 0.99 to 0.00005.

These scales are called *mated* or matched *scales* because they can be used for reciprocal values. To determine the reciprocal of a number we set it on the appropriate LL or LL0 scale and read the reciprocal on the mating scale.

Set angle on this scale	Read trigonometric on this scale	Decimal point	Examples
⎧ If the angle is converted to radians, this value ⎨ approximates the sine or tangent			
ST	C or D	0.0_ _ _	$\sin 2.5° = 0.0436$
			$\tan 1.5° = 0.0262$
S (right)	C or D	0._ _ _	$\sin 25°40' = 0.433$
S (left)	C or D	0._ _ _	$\cos 46.5° = 0.688$
Complement on ST	CI or DI	_ _._ _	$\tan 86° = 14.30$
Complement on ST	C or D	0.0_ _ _	$\cos 86° = 0.0698$
T (right)	C or D	0._ _ _	$\tan 36° = 0.726$
T (left)	CI or DI	_._ _ _	$\tan 79° = 5.145$

table C-3

Scale	Range	Scale	Range
LL1	1.01–1.105	LL01	0.99–0.905
LL2	1.105–2.718	LL02	0.905–0.369
LL3	2.718–22,026	LL03	0.369–0.00005
			(approx.)

The process of raising a number to any power involves the use of logarithms. Suppose we want to raise the number 4.13 tó the power 3.73; or, in exponential notation $4.13^{3.73}$. We might multiply the logarithm of the number 4.13 by the exponent,

$$\log 4.13 \times 3.73 = \log \text{ans}$$

This entails tedious multiplication, and we can shorten the work if we use logarithms again as follows

$$\log (\log 4.13) + \log 3.73 = \log (\log \text{ans})$$

$$4.13^{3.73} = 200$$

Here we have taken the logarithm of a logarithm. The scales designed to do this graphically on the slide rule are called *log-log scales*.

On the slide rule the same problem is easily solved by setting the hairline at 4.13 on the appropriate scale, in this case the LL3 scale; we then place the left index of the C scale under the hairline, move the hairline to the exponent 3.73 on the C scale, and read the answer under the hairline on the LL3, which is 200. Let us take another example. To find the value of $0.85^{7.5}$ we set the hairline at 0.85 on the LL02 scale, place the right index of the C scale under the hairline (we cannot use the left index and still raise the number to the 7.5 power) and move the hairline to 7.5 on the C scale, and then read answer 0.296 on the LL03 scale. Note that in this case we have jumped a scale to read the answer on the LL03 instead of the LL02 scale; this is because the scales are continuous.

Occasionally in engineering computations the answers to such problems may be larger than 22,026 or smaller than 0.00005 and hence cannot be read on the scales. When this happens we must rearrange the problem into several parts which are within the range of the scales. For example, to evaluate $345^{7.34}$ we would break the problem up into parts as follows:

$$345^{7.34} = (3.45 \times 10^2)^{7.34} = 3.45^{7.34} \times 10^{14.68}$$

$$= 3.45^{7.34} \times 10^{0.68} \times 10^{14}$$

$$= 8,800 \times 4.78 \times 10^{14}$$

$$= 42,100 \times 10^{14} = 4.21 \times 10^{18}$$

C-7 ACCURACY OF THE SLIDE RULE

In most engineering design and analysis problems the measurements usually contain two to four significant figures. It is possible to read four significant figures when the slide rule setting is between 1 and 2 and three significant figures when the value is greater than 2. This is because the scale divisions on the slide rule are not uniform, since they represent the mantissas of the logarithms of the numbers so marked. Hence as the magnitude of the number increases, it takes a smaller increase in the power of the exponent, and the scale divisions become smaller. As a general rule, in engineering computations the slide rule answer should be within ± 2 in the third significant figure. Of course, as the number of operations increases, the chance for error increases.

SLIDE-RULE EXERCISES

In the following slide-rule exercises four digits should be read on the slide rule between 1 and 2 and three digits on the rest of the scale. Each problem should be considered in two equal parts—the sequence of digits and the decimal-point location. You should be able to score at least 90 percent on each exercise for satisfactory performance.

We recommend that you record the results in the space provided, keeping the answer covered during the entire exercise. Upon completion uncover the answers and check yourself immediately.

simple multiplication

6.75	_____	C-1	450×0.0150
6.92	_____	C-2	0.197×35.2
7.62×10^6	_____	C-3	$(4.07 \times 10^5) \times (18.7)$
6.25×10^3	_____	C-4	$5,950 \times 1.05$
9.10×10^{-2}	_____	C-5	42.3×0.00215
2.35×10^{-1}	_____	C-6	3.46×0.0680
2.13	_____	C-7	0.678×3.14
5.00×10^1	_____	C-8	$(5.32 \times 10^2) \times 0.094$
1.60×10^{-6}	_____	C-9	$(4.16 \times 10^{-4}) \times (3.85 \times 10^{-3})$
1.19×10^9	_____	C-10	$(9.45 \times 10^{10}) \times (1.26 \times 10^{-2})$

simple division

4.81×10^2	_____	C-11	$\dfrac{457}{0.95}$
1.245×10^{-3}	_____	C-12	$\dfrac{0.426}{342}$
2.09×10^4	_____	C-13	$\dfrac{623}{0.0298}$
8.61×10^{-2}	_____	C-14	$\dfrac{184}{2,140}$
8.02×10^{-3}	_____	C-15	$\dfrac{622}{7.75 \times 10^6}$
4.15×10^{-3}	_____	C-16	$\dfrac{72.8}{1.75 \times 10^4}$
3.65×10^2	_____	C-17	$\dfrac{1,430}{3.92}$
3.62×10^{-2}	_____	C-18	$\dfrac{0.438}{12.1}$

C-19 $\dfrac{16.6}{0.0363}$ _____ *4.58 × 10²*

C-20 $\dfrac{93.2}{1,520}$ _____ *6.13 × 10²*

multiplication

C-21 753.2 × 1.07 × 0.0835 _____ *67.4*

C-22 75.2 × 1.73 × 0.095 _____ *12.35*

C-23 246 × 3.00 × 0.400 _____ *2.96 × 10²*

C-24 36.4 × 46.0 × 0.700 _____ *1.173 × 10³*

C-25 667 × 6.33 × 7.46 _____ *3.15 × 10⁶*

C-26 386 × 6.88 × 0.00222 _____ *5.90*

C-27 1.87 × 3.93 × 77.3 _____ *5.68 × 10²*

C-28 $(2.96 \times 10^7) \times (4.71 \times 10^{-4}) \times 1.25$ _____ *1.74 × 10⁴*

C-29 53.5 × 0.085 × 1.03 _____ *4.67*

C-30 37.2 × 47.1 × 590 × 0.00037 _____ *3.82 × 10²*

combined multiplication and division

C-31 $\dfrac{5.91 \times 143}{945 \times 0.00370}$ _____ *2.41 × 10²*

C-32 $\dfrac{0.872 \times 9780}{7.80 \times 10^4}$ _____ *1.095 × 10⁻¹*

C-33 $\dfrac{(2.85 \times 10^5) \times (8.96 \times 10^7)}{7.28 \times 10^8}$ _____ *3.51 × 10⁴*

C-34 $\dfrac{875 \times (2.63 \times 10^6)}{8.46 \times 10^5}$ _____ *2.72 × 10³*

C-35 $\dfrac{5,230 \times 1.32}{(1.40 \times 10^3) \times 93.5}$ _____ *5.28*

C-36 $\dfrac{15.5 \times (5.20 \times 10^{-1})(1.20 \times 10^{-1})}{14.7 \times 93.1}$ _____ *7.08 × 10⁻⁴*

2.23 × 10⁻¹   _____   C-37 $\dfrac{505 \times 197 \times 0.00351}{472 \times 3.33}$

5.49 × 10¹   _____   C-38 $\dfrac{444 \times 19{,}500 \times (2.30 \times 10^{-2})}{7.05 \times (1.70 \times 10^2) \times 3.02}$

6.03 × 10⁴   _____   C-39 $\dfrac{373 \times 0.0732}{(4.31 \times 10^{-4}) \times 1.05}$

49.2   _____   C-40 $\dfrac{725 \times 1.03 \times 54.5}{379 \times 2.19}$

squares

1.18 × 10⁵   _____   C-41 343^2

4.54 × 10²   _____   C-42 21.3^2

1.48 × 10⁻¹   _____   C-43 0.385^2

2.93 × 10⁶   _____   C-44 $1{,}710^2$

5.79 × 10⁵   _____   C-45 $(7.60 \times 10^2)^2$

1.44 × 10³   _____   C-46 37.9^2

9.70 × 10⁵   _____   C-47 9.85×10^2

2.46 × 10⁻⁶   _____   C-48 0.00157^2

1.87 × 10⁻⁷   _____   C-49 0.000433^2

2.80 × 10³¹   _____   C-50 $(5.29 \times 10^{15})^2$

square roots

2.41 × 10¹   _____   C-51 $580^{1/2}$

9.64   _____   C-52 $93^{1/2}$

9.88 × 10²   _____   C-53 $0.00976^{1/2}$

5.18 × 10¹   _____   C-54 $2{,}680^{1/2}$

2.73 × 10⁻²   _____   C-55 $0.000745^{1/2}$

9.94 × 10¹   _____   C-56 $9{,}890^{1/2}$

9.45 × 10⁻¹   _____   C-57 $0.892^{1/2}$

C-58 $(1.75 \times 10^{-9})^{1/2}$ _____ 4.19×10^{-5}

C-59 $(2.38 \times 10^{16})^{1/2}$ _____ 1.54×10^{8}

C-60 $(4.75 \times 10^{5})^{1/2}$ _____ 6.89×10^{2}

cubes

C-61 69^3 _____ 3.29×10^{5}

C-62 121^3 _____ 1.77×10^{6}

C-63 4.87^3 _____ 1.16×10^{2}

C-64 $(3.52 \times 10^{-3})^3$ _____ 4.36×10^{-8}

C-65 0.0847^3 _____ 6.08×10^{-4}

C-66 $(5.05 \times 10^{-9})^3$ _____ 1.29×10^{-25}

C-67 $(3.94 \times 10^{10})^3$ _____ 6.12×10^{31}

C-68 469^3 _____ 1.03×10^{8}

C-69 0.753^3 _____ 4.27×10^{-1}

C-70 979^3 _____ 9.38×10^{8}

cube roots

C-71 $959^{1/3}$ _____ 9.86

C-72 $(2.71 \times 10^3)^{1/3}$ _____ 1.39×10^{1}

C-73 $0.000374^{1/3}$ _____ 7.20×10^{-2}

C-74 $81^{1/3}$ _____ 4.33

C-75 $3.00^{1/3}$ _____ 1.44

C-76 $(3.47 \times 10^{-12})^{1/3}$ _____ 1.51×10^{-4}

C-77 $(5.91 \times 10^{-8})^{1/3}$ _____ 3.90×10^{-3}

C-78 $(6.86 \times 10^{27})^{1/3}$ _____ 1.90×10^{9}

C-79 $48,200^{1/3}$ _____ 3.64×10^{1}

C-80 $7,890^{1/3}$ _____ 1.99×10^{1}

sines

0.146	————————	*C-81*	sin 8°24'
0.585	————————	*C-82*	sin 35.8°
0.965	————————	*C-83*	sin 74°54'
0.834	————————	*C-84*	sin 56.5°
0.106	————————	*C-85*	sin 6.1°
0.992	————————	*C-86*	sin 82°36'
0.0732	————————	*C-87*	sin 4°12'
0.0139	————————	*C-88*	sin 0°48'
0.0576	————————	*C-89*	sin 3°18'
0.999	————————	*C-90*	sin 88°42'

cosines

0.947	————————	*C-91*	cos 18°42'
0.768	————————	*C-92*	cos 39.8°
0.607	————————	*C-93*	cos 52°36'
0.118	————————	*C-94*	cos 83.2°
0.0262	————————	*C-95*	cos 88°30'
0.982	————————	*C-96*	cos 10°48'
0.0122	————————	*C-97*	cos 89.3°
0.996	————————	*C-98*	cos 5°12'
0.999	————————	*C-99*	cos 2°30'
0.376	————————	*C-100*	cos 67°54'

tangents

0.543	————————	*C-101*	tan 28°30'
0.137	————————	*C-102*	tan 7°48'
1.57	————————	*C-103*	tan 57.5°

C-104	tan 83.2°	_____	8.38
C-105	tan 1°30'	_____	0.0262
C-106	tan 87.5°	_____	22.9
C-107	tan 43.8°	_____	0.960
C-108	tan 3°50'	_____	0.0670
C-109	tan 89°0'	_____	57.3
C-110	tan 0°36'	_____	0.0105

logs and log-log scales

C-111	$\log 3,735$	_____	3.572
C-112	$13.5^{3.51}$	_____	9,200
C-113	$37.3^x = 975$	_____	1.90
C-114	$3.25^{3.40}$	_____	55.6
C-115	$34.1^{2.41}$	_____	5,000
C-116	$0.752^{3.12}$	_____	0.411
C-117	$1.52^{9.76}$	_____	60
C-118	$0.822^{6.32}$	_____	0.29
C-119	$260^{5.84}$	_____	1.59×10^{14}
C-120	$0.961^{7.53}$	_____	0.741

D SUMMATION THEOREMS

Because the development of nearly all the equations in this text is in summation notation, the notation and three general cases are presented here for review.

The general form $\sum_{i=1}^{n} X_i$ is equivalent to $X_1 + X_2 + X_3 + \cdots + X_n$. In many instances the term is reduced to Σx_i, with the limits of i understood.

example The following observations represent measurements of the diameter of a steel ball taken by different members of a laboratory party:

Member i	Observation X_i, in.
1	0.511
2	0.513
3	0.512
4	0.497
5	0.498
6	0.499
7	0.492
8	0.515
9	0.500
10	0.513

If each member i of this party records an observation X, then the sum of their observations is

$$\sum_{i=1}^{10} X_i = 5.050$$

case I

Further experience with the summation conventions shows that $\sum_{i=1}^{n} C$, where C is a constant, yields nC. This is apparent in the expansion

$$C + C + C + C + \cdots + C = nC$$

or n like terms, each with the value C.

case II

A second general form of interest is where we have a constant times a variable,

$$\sum_{i=1}^{n} CA_i$$

When we expand this we obtain

$$CA_1 + CA_2 + CA_3 + \cdots + CA_n$$
$$= C(A_1 + A_2 + A_3 + \cdots + A_n)$$
$$= C \sum_{i=1}^{n} A_i$$

Therefore we can factor constants out and place them in front of the summation sign.

case III

The third general form is the addition or subtraction of two variables,

$$\sum_{i=1}^{n} (A_i \pm B_i)$$

Expansion of the case for addition yields

$$[(A_1 + B_1) + (A_2 + B_2) + \cdots + (A_n + B_n)]$$
$$= [(A_1 + A_2 + \cdots + A_n) + (B_1 + B_2 + \cdots + B_n)]$$

The first term is $\sum_{i=1}^{n} A_i$ and the second is $\sum_{i=1}^{n} B_i$. Thus

$$\sum_{i=1}^{n} (A_i + B_i) = \sum_{i=1}^{n} A_i + \sum_{i=1}^{n} B_i$$

Expansion of the case for subtraction yields

$$[(A_1 - B_1) + (A_2 - B_2) + \cdots + (A_n - B_n)]$$
$$= [(A_1 + A_2 + \cdots + A_n) - (B_1 + B_2 + \cdots + B_n)]$$

It can now be seen that

$$\sum_{i=1}^{n} (A_i - B_i) = \sum_{i=1}^{n} A_i - \sum_{i=1}^{n} B_i$$

E DERIVATION OF ERROR-PROPAGATION EQUATIONS (VARIANCES)

Although formal proof is beyond the scope of this text, the following relationship has wide application in the area of error propagation. Given a functional relationship f in terms of a, b, ..., n, where each term has its own standard error σ_m, the general equation for the variance of the function is given by

$$\sigma_m^2(f) = \left(\frac{\partial f}{\partial A} \sigma_{m_A}\right)^2 + \left(\frac{\partial f}{\partial B} \sigma_{m_B}\right)^2 + \cdots + \left(\frac{\partial f}{\partial N} \sigma_{m_N}\right)^2$$

$$E\text{-}1$$

Let us consider several applications of this general equation.

addition and subtraction

First we will look at the case discussed in Chapter Five, the difference of means. The general function is

$$f(A,B) = A - B$$

where A is a sample with mean $\bar{A}$, standard deviation σ_A, and standard error $\sigma_{m_A} = \sigma_A/\sqrt{n}$. Then

$$\sigma_{A-B}^2 = \left[\frac{\partial(A-B)}{\partial A} \sigma_{m_A}\right]^2 + \left[\frac{\partial(A-B)}{\partial B} \sigma_{m_B}\right]^2$$

$$= (1\sigma_{m_A})^2 + (-1\sigma_{m_B})^2 = \sigma_{m_A}^2 + \sigma_{m_B}^2$$

Note that

$$\sigma_{m_{A-B}}^2 = \sigma_{m_A}^2 + \sigma_{m_B}^2 = \frac{\sigma_A^2}{n} + \frac{\sigma_B^2}{n}$$

agrees with equations developed from the basic definitions in Chapter Five.

Now consider a more general case of this function for either addition or subtraction. The general function for addition or subtraction is

$$f(A,B,\ldots,N) = A \pm B \pm \cdots \pm N$$

Hence

$$\sigma_f{}^2 = \left(\frac{\partial f}{\partial A}\sigma_{m_A}\right)^2 + \left(\frac{\partial f}{\partial B}\sigma_{m_B}\right)^2 + \cdots + \left(\frac{\partial f}{\partial N}\sigma_{m_N}\right)^2$$

$$= \sigma_{m_A}^2 + \sigma_{m_B}^2 + \cdots + \sigma_{m_N}^2 \qquad\qquad \textbf{\textit{E-2}}$$

Note that the plus or minus sign affects only the derivative part and becomes positive after squaring; thus all terms are positive.

multiplication

Let us first consider the case AB then expand to a slightly more general case. The general function for multiplication of two terms is

$$f(A,B) = AB$$

Thus the variance is

$$\sigma_{AB}^2 = \left[\frac{\partial(AB)}{\partial A}\sigma_{m_A}\right]^2 + \left[\frac{\partial(AB)}{\partial B}\sigma_{m_B}\right]^2$$

$$= (B\sigma_{m_A})^2 + (A\sigma_{m_B})^2 = B^2\sigma_{m_A}^2 + A^2\sigma_{m_B}^2 \qquad \textbf{\textit{E-3}}$$

A slightly more general case,

$$f(A,B,C,D) = ABCD$$

yields

$$\sigma_{ABCD}^2 = (BCD\sigma_{m_A})^2 + (ACD\sigma_{m_B})^2 + (ABD\sigma_{m_C})^2$$
$$+ (ABC\sigma_{m_D})^2$$

$$= B^2C^2D^2\sigma_{m_A}^2 + A^2C^2D^2\sigma_{m_B}^2 + A^2B^2D^2\sigma_{m_C}^2$$
$$+ A^2B^2D^2\sigma_{m_C}^2$$

$$= A^2B^2C^2D^2\left(\frac{\sigma_{m_A}^2}{A^2} + \frac{\sigma_{m_B}^2}{B^2} + \frac{\sigma_{m_C}^2}{C^2} + \frac{\sigma_{m_D}^2}{D^2}\right) \qquad \textbf{\textit{E-4}}$$

The most general form is given without proof:

$$f(A_1,A_2,A_3,\ldots,A_n) = \prod_{i=1}^{n} A_i$$

$$\sigma_f{}^2 = \prod_{i=1}^{n} A_i^2 \left[\sum_{i=1}^{n}\left(\frac{\sigma_{m_{Ai}}}{A_i}\right)^2\right]$$

division

The simplicity we restrict ourselves to the case of A/B. The general function is

$$f(A,B) = \frac{A}{B}$$

which yields

$$\sigma_{A/B}^2 = \left[\frac{\partial(A/B)}{\partial A}\,\sigma_{m_A}\right]^2 + \left[\frac{\partial(AB^{-1})}{\partial B}\,\sigma_{m_B}\right]^2$$

$$= \left(\frac{\sigma_{m_A}}{B}\right)^2 + (-B^{-2}A\sigma_{m_B})^2 = \frac{\sigma_{m_A}^2}{B^2} + \frac{A^2}{B^4}\,\sigma_{m_B}^2$$

$$= \frac{A^2}{A^2 B^2}\,\sigma_{m_A}^2 + \frac{A^2}{B^4}\,\sigma_{m_B}^2$$

$$= \frac{A^2}{B^2}\left[\left(\frac{\sigma_{m_A}}{A}\right)^2 + \left(\frac{\sigma_{m_B}}{B}\right)^2\right] \qquad \text{E-5}$$

powers and roots

The case for powers is the same as that for multiplication except that each term is exactly the same. Since $AAA = A^3$, it is important to note that the form of the final equation is different from that given by ABC, where each term is different. For the general function

$$f(A) = A^n$$

the variance is

$$\sigma_{A^n}^2 = \left(\frac{\partial A^n}{\partial A}\,\sigma_{m_A}\right)^2 = (nA^{n-1}\sigma_{m_A})^2 \qquad \text{E-6}$$

The same observation is true of roots. For the general function

$$f(B) = B^{1/n}$$

The variance is

$$\sigma_{B^{1/n}}^2 = \left(\frac{\partial B^{1/n}}{\partial B}\,\sigma_{m_B}\right)^2 = \left(\frac{1}{n}\,B^{1/n-1}\sigma_{m_B}\right)^2$$

$$= \left(\frac{1}{n} B^{1/n} B^{-1} \sigma_{m_B} \right)^2 = \left(\frac{B^{1/n}}{nB} \sigma_{m_B} \right)^2 \qquad \text{E-7}$$

general forms

To show how general Eq. E-1 really is let us look at some functions which are combinations of the forms already presented. Consider the function

$$f(A,B) = A^2 B$$

The variance is

$$\sigma^2_{A^2 B} = \left[\frac{\partial(A^2 B)}{\partial A} \sigma_{m_A} \right]^2 + \left[\frac{\partial(A^2 B)}{\partial B} \sigma_{m_B} \right]^2$$

$$= (2AB\sigma_{m_A})^2 + (A^2\sigma_{m_B})^2$$

$$= (2AB\sigma_{m_A})^2 + (A^2\sigma_{m_B})^2$$

$$= \left(\frac{2A^2 B}{A} \sigma_{m_A} \right)^2 + \left(\frac{A^2 B}{B} \sigma_{m_B} \right)^2$$

$$= (A^2 B)^2 \left[\left(\frac{2\sigma_{m_A}}{A} \right)^2 + \left(\frac{\sigma_{m_B}}{B} \right)^2 \right]$$

For the function

$$f(A,B) = A^2 \sqrt{B}$$

it is

$$\sigma^2_{A^2\sqrt{B}} = \left[\frac{\partial(A^2\sqrt{B})}{\partial A} \sigma_{m_A} \right]^2 + \left[\frac{\partial(A^2\sqrt{B})}{\partial B} \sigma_{m_B} \right]^2$$

$$= (2A\sqrt{B}\sigma_{m_A})^2 + \left(\frac{A^2}{2\sqrt{B}} \sigma_{m_B} \right)^2$$

Once the general solutions for addition, subtraction, multiplication, division, powers, and roots are known, we can also use simple algebra to find the variance of combined forms. Examples are given in Chapter Six.

n	$n!$	$\log n!$	n	$n!$	$\log n!$
			50	3.0414×10^{64}	64.48307
1	1.0000	0.00000	51	1.5511×10^{66}	66.19065
2	2.0000	0.30103	52	8.0658×10^{67}	67.90665
3	6.0000	0.77815	53	4.2749×10^{69}	69.63092
4	2.4000×10	1.38021	54	2.3084×10^{71}	71.36332
5	1.2000×10^2	2.07918	55	1.2696×10^{73}	73.10368
6	7.2000×10^2	2.85733	56	7.1100×10^{74}	74.85187
7	5.0400×10^3	3.70243	57	4.0527×10^{76}	76.60774
8	4.0320×10^4	4.60552	58	2.3506×10^{78}	78.37117
9	3.6288×10^5	5.55976	59	1.3868×10^{80}	80.14202
10	3.6288×10^6	6.55976	60	8.3210×10^{81}	81.92017
11	3.9917×10^7	7.60116	61	5.0758×10^{83}	83.70550
12	4.7900×10^8	8.68034	62	3.1470×10^{85}	85.49790
13	6.2270×10^9	9.79428	63	1.9826×10^{87}	87.29724
14	8.7178×10^{10}	10.94041	64	1.2689×10^{89}	89.10342
15	1.3077×10^{12}	12.11650	65	8.2477×10^{90}	90.91633
16	2.0923×10^{13}	13.32062	66	5.4435×10^{92}	92.73587
17	3.5569×10^{14}	14.55107	67	3.6471×10^{94}	94.56195
18	6.4024×10^{15}	15.80634	68	2.4800×10^{96}	96.39446
19	1.2165×10^{17}	17.08509	69	1.7112×10^{98}	98.23331
20	2.4329×10^{18}	18.38612	70	1.1979×10^{100}	100.07841
21	5.1091×10^{19}	19.70834	71	8.5048×10^{101}	101.92966
22	1.1240×10^{21}	21.05077	72	6.1234×10^{103}	103.78700
23	2.5852×10^{22}	22.41249	73	4.4701×10^{105}	105.65032
24	6.2045×10^{23}	23.79271	74	3.3079×10^{107}	107.51955
25	1.5511×10^{25}	25.19065	75	2.4809×10^{109}	109.39461
26	4.0329×10^{26}	26.60562	76	1.8855×10^{111}	111.27543
27	1.0889×10^{28}	28.03698	77	1.4518×10^{113}	113.16192
28	3.0489×10^{29}	29.48414	78	1.1324×10^{115}	115.05401
29	8.8418×10^{30}	30.94654	79	8.9462×10^{116}	116.95164
30	2.6525×10^{32}	32.42366	80	7.1569×10^{118}	118.85473
31	8.2228×10^{33}	33.91502	81	5.7971×10^{120}	120.76321
32	2.6313×10^{35}	35.42017	82	4.7536×10^{122}	122.67703
33	8.6833×10^{36}	36.93869	83	3.9455×10^{124}	124.59610
34	2.9523×10^{38}	38.47016	84	3.3142×10^{126}	126.52038
35	1.0333×10^{40}	40.01423	85	2.8171×10^{128}	128.44980
36	3.7199×10^{41}	41.57054	86	2.4227×10^{130}	130.38430
37	1.3764×10^{43}	43.13874	87	2.1078×10^{132}	132.32382
38	5.2302×10^{44}	44.71852	88	1.8548×10^{134}	134.26830
39	2.0398×10^{46}	46.30959	89	1.6508×10^{136}	136.21769
40	8.1592×10^{47}	47.91165	90	1.4857×10^{138}	138.17194
41	3.3453×10^{49}	49.52443	91	1.3520×10^{140}	140.13098
42	1.4050×10^{51}	51.14768	92	1.2438×10^{142}	142.09477
43	6.0415×10^{52}	52.78115	93	1.1568×10^{144}	144.06325
44	2.6583×10^{54}	54.42460	94	1.0874×10^{146}	146.03638
45	1.1962×10^{56}	56.07781	95	1.0330×10^{148}	148.01410
46	5.5026×10^{57}	57.74057	96	9.9168×10^{149}	149.99637
47	2.5862×10^{59}	59.41267	97	9.6193×10^{151}	151.98314
48	1.2414×10^{61}	61.09391	98	9.4269×10^{153}	153.97437
49	6.0828×10^{62}	62.78410	99	9.3326×10^{155}	155.97000
50	3.0414×10^{64}	64.48307	100	9.3326×10^{157}	157.97000

SOURCE: "Handbook of Chemistry and Physics," 7th ed., Chemical Rubber Publishing Co., Cleveland, Ohio, 1946.

G AREAS UNDER THE NORMAL-DISTRIBUTION CURVE FROM $\bar{X}_0$ TO Z (ONE SIDE)

$Z = (x_i - \bar{X})/\sigma_s$	.00	.01	.02	.03	.04	.05	.06	.07	.08	.09
0.0	.0000	.0040	.0080	.0120	.0160	.0199	.0239	.0279	.0319	.0359
0.1	.0398	.0438	.0478	.0517	.0557	.0596	.0636	.0675	.0714	.0753
0.2	.0793	.0832	.0871	.0910	.0948	.0987	.1026	.1064	.1103	.1141
0.3	.1179	.1217	.1255	.1293	.1331	.1368	.1406	.1443	.1480	.1517
0.4	.1554	.1591	.1628	.1664	.1700	.1736	.1772	.1808	.1844	.1879
0.5	.1915	.1950	.1985	.2019	.2054	.2088	.2123	.2157	.2190	.2224
0.6	.2257	.2291	.2324	.2357	.2389	.2422	.2454	.2486	.2517	.2549
0.7	.2580	.2611	.2642	.2673	.2704	.2734	.2764	.2794	.2823	.2852
0.8	.2881	.2910	.2939	.2967	.2995	.3023	.3051	.3078	.3106	.3233
0.9	.3159	.3186	.3212	.3238	.3264	.3289	.3315	.3340	.3365	.3389
1.0	.3413	.3438	.3461	.3485	.3508	.3531	.3554	.3577	.3599	.3621
1.1	.3643	.3665	.3686	.3708	.3729	.3749	.3770	.3790	.3810	.3830
1.2	.3849	.3869	.3888	.3907	.3925	.3944	.3962	.3980	.3997	.4015
1.3	.4032	.4049	.4066	.4082	.4099	.4115	.4131	.4147	.4162	.4177
1.4	.4192	.4207	.4222	.4236	.4251	.4265	.4279	.4292	.4306	.4319
1.5	.4332	.4345	.4357	.4370	.4382	.4394	.4406	.4418	.4429	.4441
1.6	.4452	.4463	.4474	.4484	.4495	.4505	.4515	.4525	.4535	.4545
1.7	.4554	.4564	.4573	.4582	.4591	.4599	.4608	.4616	.4625	.4633
1.8	.4641	.4649	.4656	.4664	.4671	.4678	.4686	.4693	.4699	.4706
1.9	.4713	.4719	.4726	.4732	.4738	.4744	.4750	.4758	.4761	.4767
2.0	.4772	.4778	.4783	.4788	.4793	.4798	.4803	.4808	.4812	.4817
2.1	.4821	.4826	.4830	.4834	.4838	.4842	.4846	.4850	.4854	.4857
2.2	.4861	.4864	.4868	.4871	.4875	.4878	.4881	.4884	.4887	.4890
2.3	.4893	.4896	.4898	.4901	.4904	.4906	.4909	.4911	.4913	.4916
2.4	.4918	.4920	.4922	.4925	.4927	.4929	.4931	.4932	.4934	.4936
2.5	.4938	.4940	.4941	.4943	.4945	.4946	.4948	.4949	.4951	.4952
2.6	.4953	.4955	.4956	.4957	.4959	.4960	.4961	.4962	.4963	.4964
2.7	.4965	.4966	.4967	.4968	.4969	.4970	.4971	.4972	.4973	.4974
2.8	.4974	.4975	.4976	.4977	.4977	.4978	.4979	.4979	.4980	.4981
2.9	.4981	.4982	.4982	.4983	.4984	.4984	.4985	.4985	.4986	.4986
3.0	.49865	.4987	.4987	.4988	.4989	.4988	.4989	.4989	.4989	.4990

SOURCE: Edward C. Bryant, "Statistical Analysis," McGraw-Hill Book Company, New York, 1966.

G AREAS UNDER THE NORMAL-DISTRIBUTION CURVE FROM Z TO ∞ (ONE SIDE)

$$Z = (x_i - \overline{X})/\sigma_s$$

	.00	.01	.02	.03	.04	.05	.06	.07	.08	.09
0.0	.5000	.4960	.4920	.4880	.4840	.4801	.4761	.4721	.4681	.4641
0.1	.4602	.4562	.4522	.4483	.4443	.4404	.4364	.4325	.4286	.4247
0.2	.4207	.4168	.4129	.4090	.4052	.4013	.3974	.3936	.3897	.3859
0.3	.3821	.3783	.3745	.3707	.3669	.3632	.3594	.3557	.3520	.3483
0.4	.3446	.3409	.3372	.3336	.3300	.3264	.3228	.3192	.3156	.3121
0.5	.3085	.3050	.3015	.2981	.2946	.2912	.2877	.2843	.2810	.2776
0.6	.2743	.2709	.2676	.2643	.2611	.2578	.2546	.2514	.2483	.2451
0.7	.2420	.2389	.2358	.2327	.2296	.2266	.2236	.2206	.2177	.2148
0.8	.2119	.2090	.2061	.2033	.2005	.1977	.1949	.1922	.1894	.1867
0.9	.1841	.1814	.1788	.1762	.1736	.1711	.1685	.1660	.1635	.1611
1.0	.1587	.1562	.1539	.1515	.1492	.1469	.1446	.1423	.1401	.1379
1.1	.1357	.1335	.1314	.1292	.1271	.1251	.1230	.1210	.1190	.1170
1.2	.1151	.1131	.1112	.1093	.1075	.1056	.1038	.1020	.1003	.0985
1.3	.0968	.0951	.0934	.0918	.0901	.0885	.0869	.0853	.0838	.0823
1.4	.0808	.0793	.0778	.0764	.0749	.0735	.0721	.0708	.0694	.0681
1.5	.0668	.0655	.0643	.0630	.0618	.0606	.0594	.0582	.0571	.0559
1.6	.0548	.0537	.0526	.0516	.0505	.0495	.0485	.0475	.0465	.0455
1.7	.0446	.0436	.0427	.0418	.0409	.0401	.0392	.0384	.0375	.0367
1.8	.0359	.0351	.0344	.0336	.0329	.0322	.0314	.0307	.0301	.0294
1.9	.0287	.0281	.0274	.0268	.0262	.0256	.0250	.0244	.0239	.0233
2.0	.0228	.0222	.0217	.0212	.0207	.0202	.0197	.0192	.0188	.0183
2.1	.0179	.0174	.0170	.0166	.0162	.0158	.0154	.0150	.0146	.0143
2.2	.0139	.0136	.0132	.0129	.0125	.0122	.0119	.0116	.0113	.0110
2.3	.0107	.0104	.0102	.00990	.00964	.00939	.00914	.00889	.00866	.00842
2.4	.00820	.00798	.00776	.00755	.00734	.00714	.00695	.00676	.00657	.00639
2.5	.00621	.00604	.00587	.00570	.00554	.00539	.00523	.00508	.00494	.00480
2.6	.00466	.00453	.00440	.00427	.00415	.00402	.00391	.00379	.00368	.00357
2.7	.00347	.00336	.00326	.00317	.00307	.00298	.00298	.00280	.00272	.00264
2.8	.00256	.00248	.00240	.00233	.00226	.00219	.00212	.00205	.00199	.00193
2.9	.00187	.00181	.00175	.00169	.00164	.00159	.00154	.00149	.00144	.00139

SOURCE: Frederick E. Croxton, "Elementary Statistics with Applications in Medicine," Prentice-Hall, Inc., Englewood Cliffs, N.J., 1953, p. 323.

238

H ORDINATES (f) OF THE STANDARD NORMAL CURVE AT Z

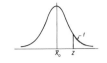

Z	0	1	2	3	4	5	6	7	8	9
0.0	.3989	.3989	.3989	.3988	.3986	.3984	.3982	.3980	.3977	.3973
0.1	.3970	.3965	.3961	.3956	.3951	.3945	.3939	.3932	.3925	.3918
0.2	.3910	.3902	.3894	.3885	.3876	.3867	.3857	.3847	.3836	.3825
0.3	.3814	.3802	.3790	.3778	.3765	.3752	.3739	.3725	.3712	.3697
0.4	.3683	.3668	.3653	.3637	.3621	.3605	.3589	.3572	.3555	.3538
0.5	.3521	.3503	.3485	.3467	.3448	.3429	.3410	.3391	.3372	.3352
0.6	.3332	.3312	.3292	.3271	.3251	.3230	.3209	.3187	.3166	.3144
0.7	.3123	.3101	.3079	.3056	.3034	.3011	.2989	.2966	.2943	.2920
0.8	.2897	.2874	.2850	.2827	.2803	.2780	.2756	.2732	.2709	.2685
0.9	.2661	.2637	.2613	.2589	.2565	.2541	.2516	.2492	.2468	.2444
1.0	.2420	.2396	.2371	.2347	.2323	.2299	.2275	.2251	.2227	.2203
1.1	.2179	.2155	.2131	.2107	.2083	.2059	.2036	.2012	.1989	.1965
1.2	.1942	.1919	.1895	.1872	.1849	.1826	.1804	.1781	.1758	.1736
1.3	.1714	.1691	.1669	.1647	.1626	.1604	.1582	.1561	.1539	.1518
1.4	.1497	.1476	.1456	.1435	.1415	.1394	.1374	.1354	.1334	.1315
1.5	.1295	.1276	.1257	.1238	.1219	.1200	.1182	.1163	.1145	.1127
1.6	.1109	.1092	.1074	.1057	.1040	.1023	.1006	.0989	.0973	.0957
1.7	.0940	.0925	.0909	.0893	.0878	.0863	.0848	.0833	.0818	.0804
1.8	.0790	.0775	.0761	.0748	.0734	.0721	.0707	.0694	.0681	.0669
1.9	.0656	.0644	.0632	.0620	.0608	.0596	.0584	.0573	.0562	.0551
2.0	.0540	.0529	.0519	.0508	.0498	.0488	.0478	.0468	.0459	.0499
2.1	.0440	.0431	.0422	.0413	.0404	.0396	.0387	.0379	.0371	.0363
2.2	.0355	.0347	.0339	.0332	.0325	.0317	.0310	.0303	.0297	.0290
2.3	.0283	.0277	.0270	.0264	.0258	.0252	.0246	.0241	.0235	.0229
2.4	.0224	.0219	.0213	.0208	.0203	.0198	.0194	.0189	.0184	.0180
2.5	.0175	.0171	.0167	.0163	.0158	.0154	.0151	.0147	.0143	.0139
2.6	.0136	.0132	.0129	.0126	.0122	.0119	.0116	.0113	.0110	.0107
2.7	.0104	.0101	.0099	.0096	.0093	.0091	.0088	.0086	.0084	.0081
2.8	.0079	.0077	.0075	.0073	.0071	.0069	.0067	.0065	.0063	.0061
2.9	.0060	.0058	.0056	.0055	.0053	.0051	.0050	.0048	.0047	.0046
3.0	.0044	.0043	.0042	.0040	.0039	.0038	.0037	.0036	.0035	.0034
3.1	.0033	.0032	.0031	.0030	.0029	.0028	.0027	.0026	.0025	.0025
3.2	.0024	.0023	.0022	.0022	.0021	.0020	.0020	.0019	.0018	.0018
3.3	.0017	.0017	.0016	.0016	.0015	.0015	.0014	.0014	.0013	.0013
3.4	.0012	.0012	.0012	.0011	.0011	.0010	.0010	.0010	.0009	.0009
3.5	.0009	.0008	.0008	.0008	.0008	.0007	.0007	.0007	.0007	.0006
3.6	.0006	.0006	.0006	.0005	.0005	.0005	.0005	.0005	.0005	.0004
3.7	.0004	.0004	.0004	.0004	.0004	.0004	.0003	.0003	.0003	.0003
3.8	.0003	.0003	.0003	.0003	.0003	.0002	.0002	.0002	.0002	.0002
3.9	.0002	.0002	.0002	.0002	.0002	.0002	.0002	.0002	.0001	.0001

SOURCE: Murray R. Spiegel, "Schaum's Outline Series: Theory and Problems of Statistics," McGraw-Hill Book Company, New York, 1961.

references

Barry, Austin B.: "Engineering Measurements," John Wiley & Sons, Inc., New York, 1964. (General text on measurements)

Bridgman, P. W.: "Dimensional Analysis," Yale University Press, Cambridge, Mass., 1963. (Specialized text on dimensional analysis)

Ipsen, D. C.: "Units, Dimensions and Dimensionless Numbers," McGraw-Hill Book Company, New York, 1960. (Specialized text on dimensionless analysis)

Pankhurst, R. C.: "Dimensional Analysis and Scale Factors," Chapman and Hall Ltd., London; Reinhold Publishing Corporation, New York, 1964. (Specialized text on dimensional analysis)

Topping, J.: "Errors of Observation and Their Treatment," Chapman and Hall Ltd., London; Reinhold Publishing Corporation, New York, 1960. (General text on error propagation)

Wolff, Martin: "Dimensions and Unit Systems," University of Washington Press, Seattle, Wash., 1965. (General text on dimensional analysis)

Bowker, A. H., and G. J. Lieberman: "Engineering Statistics," Prentice-Hall, Inc., Englewood Cliffs, N.J., 1959. (Advanced text on statistics)

Hald, A.: "Statistical Theory and Engineering Applications," John Wiley & Sons, Inc., New York, 1952. (Excellent coverage of advanced statistics)

Hahn, G. J., and S. S. Shapiro: "Statistical Models in Engineering," John Wiley & Sons, Inc., New York, 1967. (Advanced text showing many engineering applications)

Freund, John E.: "Mathematical Statistics," Prentice-Hall, Inc., Englewood Cliffs, N.J., 1962. (Mathematical coverage of probability and statistics)

Miller, I., and J. E. Freund: "Probability and Statistics for Engineers," Prentice-Hall, Inc., Englewood Cliffs, N.J., 1965. (Advanced text in probability and statistics)

answers

CHAPTER 1

1-1 Size, quantity, position, and time

1-2 Correctness or truth

1-3 Reproducibility

1-4 The dispersion around a mean may be very small, yet the mean may be incorrect

1-5 Yes. The mean may approach the true value even though the set has greater dispersion

1-6 Accuracy good; Precision indeterminate

1-7 Direct and indirect

1-8 Repeat them

1-9 By comparison with a higher standard

1-10 Because in the comparison with a predefined standard they ultimately require a readout

1-11 Unit

1-12 Comparison of an unknown with a predefined standard

1-13 Poor

1-14 Its error

1-15 *a* Accurate and precise

  b Precise but not accurate

CHAPTER 2

2-1 99.98 ft

2-2 835.00 ft

2-3 328.21 ft

2-4 59.95 ft × 94.92 ft

2-5 Cumulative

2-6 Random or compensating

2-7 $E_a = 0.3$ ft; $E_r = 0.00317$; $E_p = 0.317$ percent

2-8 $E_p = 0.5$ percent; $E_a = 0.078$ ohms; $E_r = 0.005$

2-9 1.257 and 1.243

2-10 $E_a = 0.005$ in.; $E_r = 0.008$; $E_p = 0.8$ percent

2-11 (A) $E_a = 0.005; E_r = 0.0057; E_p = 0.57$ percent
(B) $E_a = 0.005; E_r = 0.0057; E_p = 0.57$ percent
Neither; they all were the same

2-12 $E_p = 0.2$ percent

2-13 5.94 ft × 7.92 ft × 9.90 ft

2-14 a 146 psi   d 0 psi
b 97 psi   e 72.5 psi
c 48 psi   f 121.5 psi

2-15 1.17 ft

2-16 0.343 ft

2-17 $E_r = 0.00104$

2-18 1,323.30 ft

2-19 25 ft $3\frac{9}{16}$ in.

2-20 a 4.33   e 0.408
b 0.935   f 9.33
c 70.0×10^{-3} g 2.79
d 3.85   h 3.14

2-21 a 3   g 3   m 4
b 4   h 2   n 1
c 3   i 4   o 5
d 2   j 4   p 4
e 2   k 3   q 1 or 2
f 2   l 5   r 6

2-22 a 60   f 476
b 3.95   g 0.0008
c 0.098   h 35,000
d 0.0035   i 36,000
e 15   j 500

2-23 a 39.90 cm
b 39.7 cm
c 39.8 cm
d Sometimes the results differ due to cumulative rounding errors and in the use of the addition rule

2-24 a 0.005 mi
b 0.0000005 cm
c 50 microns

2-25 *a* 36.39222 ft
    b 36.2 ft
    c 36.38 ft
    d Sometimes the results differ due to cumulative rounding errors and in the use of the addition rule

2-26 *a* 28.0
    b 13.36

2-27 *a* 70,700
    b 0.0792
    c 3,565.07
    d -0.02

2-28 *a* 5.86×10^3
    b 7.3×10^2
    c 6×10^5

2-29 *a* 1.6×10^4
    b 6.89×10^{-3}
    c 2.000×10^{-6}

2-30 125.02 ft $\times$ 157.53 ft

CHAPTER 3

3-1 *a* $\frac{1}{2}$ *b* $\frac{1}{2}$ *c* $\frac{1}{3}$ *d* $\frac{1}{6}$ *e* 0   *f* 0

3-3 *a* $\frac{1}{26}$ *b* $\frac{1}{2}$ *c* $\frac{4}{13}$ *d* $\frac{1}{13}$

3-4 $\frac{1}{5,520}$

3-5 $\frac{1}{36}$

3-6 0

3-7 $\frac{1}{18}$

3-8 $\frac{4}{663}; \frac{1}{169}$

3-10 *a* $\frac{125}{1,296}$ *b* $\frac{25}{1,296}$ *c* $\frac{5}{1,296}$ *d* $\frac{1}{1,296}$ *e* $\frac{625}{1,296}$

3-12 Not the same

3-13 *a* 0.74   *b* 0   *c* 0   *d* 0.26

3-14 *a* 0.56   *b* 0.09   *c* 0.45   *d* 0.44

3-15 0.88

3-16 0.81; 0.99

3-17 0.025; 0.01

3-18 a $\frac{300}{1,190}$ b $\frac{300}{1,190}$ c $\frac{600}{1,190}$ d $\frac{380}{1,190}$ e $\frac{210}{1,190}$

3-19 9×10^{-5}

3-20 $\frac{1}{8}$

3-21 3 percent

3-22 Probably not based on economics alone

3-23 Usage $= \dfrac{\text{no. of failures in replenishment period}}{\text{total no. of items in use during replenishment period}}$

3-24 $(3)^{20}; (\frac{1}{3})^{20}$

3-25 870

3-26 80

3-27 40,320 to 1

3-28 a 3.63×10^6
  b 3,024
  c 3.5569×10^{14}
  d 1.18×10^{33}
  e 1.15×10^{14}

3-29 a 120
  b 5.0×10^3
  c 5.08×10^9
  d 4.21×10^{22}

3-30 30,250

3-31 2,598,960

3-33 $6.7 \times 10^{11}; 1.84 \times 10^5$

3-34 5.94×10^4

3-35 630; 420

3-36 0.12; 0.945

3-37 $1.54 \times 10^{-1}; \frac{64}{625}$

3-38 3.87×10^{-1}

3-39 2,000

CHAPTER 4

4-1 $\overline{X} = 1.9$ in.; $\sigma_s = 0.1$ in.

4-2 a No
  b Yes
  c No
  d No

4-3 $\overline{X} \simeq 60$ ohms; $R = 20$ ohms

4-4 *a* $\overline{X} = 6.16$; $\tilde{X} = 6$; Mode $= 6$

  b $\overline{X} = 6.63$; $\tilde{X} = 6.5$; Mode $= 6$

4-5 $\overline{X} = 7.11$; $\tilde{X} = 6.95$; Mode $= 6.8$; $R = 1.5$; $\sigma_s = 0.468$

4-6 $\overline{X} = 4.75$ in.; $\tilde{X} = 4.7$ in.; Mode $= 4.7$ in.;

$R = 0.70$ in.; Class interval $= 0.1$ in.

4-8 $\overline{X} = 2.616$ millisec; $\tilde{X} = 2.615$ millisec; $\sigma_s = 0.0841$ millisec;

Yes

4-9 $\overline{X} = 2.539$ cm; $\tilde{X} = 2.54$ cm; Mode $= 2.54$ cm;

$R = 0.06$ cm; $\sigma_s = 0.0136$ cm

4-10 $\overline{X} = 74°$; $\sigma_s = 2.32°$

4-11 Prestressed $\overline{X} = 6.485$ kips; $\sigma_s = 1.174$ kips

Conventional $\overline{X} = 3.963$ kips; $\sigma_s = 0.566$ kips

4-12 $\overline{X} = 0.2363$ in.; $\tilde{X} = 0.235$ in.; Mode $= 0.235$ in.;

$\sigma_s = 0.00867$ in.

4-13 $\overline{X}_1 = 148.7$ lb $\sigma_1 = 4.22$ lb

  $\overline{X}_2 = 151.1$ lb $\sigma_2 = 4.22$ lb

  $\overline{X}_3 = 152.4$ lb $\sigma_3 = 4.92$ lb

  $\overline{X}_4 = 155.4$ lb $\sigma_4 = 4.38$ lb

  $\overline{X}_{tot} = 151.9$ lb $\sigma_{tot} = 5.08$ lb

4-14 $\overline{X} = 0.140$ sec; $\sigma_s = 0.0078$ sec

4-15 42 percent. The excess demand is during the summer, so we could ration water, build storage for excess of other months, etc.

4-16

	Loading	Haul	Spread	Return
$\overline{X}$	1.313	2.499	1.632	1.900
σ_s	0.232	0.176	0.125	0.134

It appears the loading phase is the most variable

4-17 $\overline{X}_{tot} = 7.344$; $\sigma_{tot} = 0.392$

4-18 $\overline{X} = 12.53$ mg; $\sigma_s = 0.218$ mg; $\tilde{X} = 12.6$ mg;

Mode $= 12.6$ mg

4-19 $\overline{X} = 621.89$ millisec; $\sigma_s = 6.9$ millisec; $\tilde{X} = 620$ millisec;

Mode $= 620$ millisec

CHAPTER 5

5-2 38 years

5-3 51 students

5-4   11.0 percent
5-5   89.0 percent
5-6   72 tubes
5-7   93 percent
5-8   34,150 contacts; 2,300 contacts
5-9   683 bulbs; 23 bulbs; 136 bulbs
5-10   2.28 percent
5-11   818 resistors; 136 resistors; 23 resistors; Limits of acceptability, 251 to 349 ohms
5-12   50.6 ohms
5-13 $\bar{X} = 152.1$ knots; $\sigma_s = 8.9$ knots; $\tilde{X} = 155$ knots; $\sigma_m = 1.06$ knots; 137.2 to 166.7 knots
5-14 $\bar{X} = 8.17$ years; $\sigma_s = 3.18$ years; $\sigma_m = 0.650$ years; $R = 12$ years; $\tilde{X} = 8$ years; Mode $= 8$ years
5-15 $\bar{X} = 152.7°$; $\sigma_s = 10.1°$; $\tilde{X} = 155°$; $\sigma_m = 1.17°$
5-16 $\bar{X} = 35.74$ millisec; $\sigma_s = 0.292$ millisec; $\tilde{X} = 35.7$ millisec; $\sigma_m = 0.0301$ millisec
5-17   2.28 percent; 1,279 to 1,481 days
5-18 $\bar{X} = 2.5425$ in.; $\sigma_s = 0.1$ in.; 818 diameters; 0 to 1 diameter
5-19   No, since 0.3063 in. falls within the range
5-20 $\bar{X} = 7.9$ hr; $\sigma_s = 0.864$ hr; $\tilde{X} = 8.0$ hr; mode $= 7.5$, 7.3 to 8.5 hr
5-21 $\sigma_m = 0.465°$; 73.2°; 74.72°
5-22   No, because the $\sigma_s = 9.0$ is much too large for a range of 18
5-23   Yes, because it is outside the limits of the normal distribution
5-24 $\sigma_s = 12$ in.; $n = 64$
5-25   3210 ± 29.6 lb; 2,979 lb
5-26   Actual difference 2.522 is greater than 0.71, and so prestressing is superior
5-27   Since actual difference 1.0 is greater than 0.774, there is a significant difference
5-28   69.54 in. to 70.70 in.
5-29   Since actual difference 0.5 is greater than 0.446, brand B gives significantly more mileage
5-30   Since actual difference 7 is greater than 6.28, they are significantly different
5-31   Since actual difference 4.0 is less than 4.8, there is no significant difference

5-32 Since actual difference 0.08 is greater than 0.0574, they are significantly different

5-33 $\bar{X}_I = 0.462$ $\sigma_{sI} = 0.026$
$\bar{X}_{II} = 0.473$ $\sigma_{sII} = 0.025$
Yes, since actual difference 0.011 is greater than 0.0092 they are significantly different

5-34 Since actual difference 3 is less than 3.4, there is no significant difference

5-35 Since actual difference 20 is greater than 18.9, they are significantly different

5-36 Since actual difference 0.9 is less than 1.006, they are not significantly different.

CHAPTER 6

6-1 408.09 ± 0.006 ft
6-2 $35°43'39'' \pm 5''$
6-3 ± 1.41 ft^2
6-4 ± 3.24 in.^{3}
6-5 0.0005
6-6 300.00 ± 1.75 ft^2
6-7 20.00 ± 0.0269 ft
6-8 $4,690 \pm 205$ cm^3
6-9 a ± 0.14 in.
   b ± 0.25 in.^{2}
   c ± 0.19 in.^{2}
6-10 113.2 ± 4.5 cm^3
6-11 268 ± 4 in.^{3}
6-12 220 ± 3.64 cm^2
6-13 ± 3.14 in.^{3}
6-14 6.20 in.^{5}
6-15 0.00144 sec
6-16 $\hat{y}_i = 0.37 + 1.31x$; $\hat{y} = 0.37 + 1.31x \pm 34.8$ at 90 percent confidence
6-17 Horsepower $= 76.61 + 0.0436$ (rpm); not reasonable because the equation states that there is 77 horsepower when the engine is

not turning. The results are limited to the operating range of the engine since we expect 0 horsepower at 0 rpm; 186.5 to 227.5 horsepower at 95 percent confidence; 260 horsepower at 4,200 rpm

6-18 $n = 2$

6-19 $a = 0, b = 1; a = -0.280, b = 1.03$. Predicted values seem to be quite close to expected values. Note that both a and b indicate that grades are slightly lower than predicted. Range 2.3 to 3.6

CHAPTER 7

7-1   a $\dfrac{FT^2}{L^4}$ b N   c $\dfrac{FL}{T}$ d FL   e $\dfrac{F}{L^2}$

7-2   a $\dfrac{M}{L^3}$ b N   c $\dfrac{ML^2}{T^3}$ d $\dfrac{ML^2}{T^2}$ e $\dfrac{M}{T^2 L}$

7-3   7,700 km/week

7-4 5.93×10^8 ft-lb$_f$

7-5 1.01×10^{10} cm^2

7-6   2.04 ton/hr

7-7 1.07×10^8 m/hr

7-8 $[K] = $ ft

7-9 $[S] = $ ft^2; $[C] = $ sec

7-10 $[G] = \dfrac{L^3}{MT^2}$; $[G] = \dfrac{L^4}{FT^4}$

7-11 $[C] = L$; $[S] = \dfrac{L}{T^2}$

7-12 $\dfrac{F}{L^2} \neq \dfrac{F}{L}$; No

7-13 $[X] = $ lb$_f$/ft^2

7-14   Yes

7-15 $[X] = L$

7-16   Yes

7-17 $[f] = $ N

7-18   Yes

7-19   Yes

7-20 $[y] = $ ft

7-21 $[S] = L$

7-22 $[A] = F; [K] = F^{7/5}$

7-23 $[C] = \dfrac{T}{L^{23/5}}$

7-24 $[a] = L^3; [R] = \dfrac{F}{T}; [S] = \dfrac{F}{T^2}$

7-25 $[r] = \dfrac{T}{L}; [A] = N$

7-26 $[R] = F; n = 4; [S] = L^4$

7-27 $[D] = T; n = 4; [B] = F; y = 8; [E] = \dfrac{T^4}{F^8}$

7-28 $[X] = F; [Y] = T; [Z] = \dfrac{F^6}{T^3}; n = 6; d = 3$

7-29 871 lb_m

7-30 2,330 lb_f

7-31 Moon: 8,780 slugs; 2.83×10^5 lb_m
Earth: 8,780 slugs; 2.83×10^5 lb_f

7-32 19.8 slugs

7-33 1,970 lb_m

7-34 1.48×10^3 lb_f

7-35 2.35×10^3 slugs

7-36 1.96×10^3 in./sec^2

7-37   *a*   3.25 lb_m
      b   0.101 slugs
      c   3.25 lb_m
      d   12.2 ft/sec^2

7-38   *a*   100 lb_m
      b   100 lb_m
      c   3.11 slugs
      d   146.2 lb_f

7-39   *a*   150 lb_m
      b   150 lb_m
      c   4.66 slugs
      d   229 lb_f

7-40   *a*   120,000 lb_f

    b   20,000 lb_f

    c   120,000 lb_m

    d   3,750 slugs

    e   12,200 lb_f

7-41   *a*   6.75 ft/sec^2

    b   220,000 lb_f

    c   8,810 slugs

7-42 7.00×10^3 lb_f

7-43   *a*   3.48 lb_m

    b   3.48 lb_f

    c   0.651 lb_f

    d   3.48 lb_m

7-44   *a*   10.7 lb_m

    b   0.332 slugs

    c   10.7 lb_m

    d   12.7 ft/sec^2

7-45   On Mars $g = 12.9$ ft/sec^2; On Jupiter $g = 86.8$ ft/sec^2

7-46   *a*   850 lb_f

    b   850 lb_m

    c   2.22 lb_f

index